KING ARTHUR AND HIS KNIGHTS

KING ARTHUR

AND

HIS KNIGHTS

BY MABEL LOUISE ROBINSON

Illustrated by DOUGLAS GORSLINE

RANDOM HOUSE · NEW YORK

THIRD PRINTING

Copyright 1953 by Mabel Louise Robinson
All rights reserved under International
and Pan-American Copyright Conventions

Published in New York by Random House, Inc.
and simultaneously in Toronto, Canada by
Random House of Canada Ltd.

Library of Congress Catalog Card Number: 53–6268
Manufactured in the U.S.A.

CONTENTS

Foreword

King Arthur's Place in the World

BACK IN THE SIXTH CENTURY THE BRITISH ISLES WERE NOT
as they are now. England, Ireland, Scotland, Wales, all were
divided up into small kingdoms each with its own ruler, each
looking for trouble. They fought together, won or lost their
lands, shifted their boundaries, until, as one writer says, we
need the magic of Merlin to set us straight about the places.

But here on this island of Great Britain the conditions

under which men lived were much the same in all of the kingdoms. Most of the people were poor beyond belief, and moreover they had no possible way of escaping from that plight of poverty. They were in a complete state of slavery to the rich.

Naturally enough, among the rich there was a constant struggle for power. The poor worked for them so that they had nothing else to do except to increase their riches. All their power lay in the amount of wealth to which they could lay claim.

Since they could not come by their wealth by hard work because the poor released them from that necessity, there was of course no way of increasing riches except by seizing each other's property. And since no one would allow his property to be taken from him without protest, the struggle for possession kept men fighting. Their real work was fighting and they did it with pleasure. Their reward was more lands which sooner or later somebody would take away from them. Their honors were all based on skill with the sword.

Out of this constant struggle, and the honors and wealth attached to victory, were bound to arise certain standards. Because the strong could win the battle, there was a real worship of physical strength. There was no place in the world for the weak of body even if the mind was strong. The dependence upon the sword for power meant dependence upon enough strength to wield it. For this a man did not need judgment and wisdom as much as he needed blind courage and brawn.

Then because of the standards which worshipped strength there was no need or demand for that high quality of liv-

ing, Justice. To decide upon the justice of a matter we try
to weigh and consider all sides of it. Then we make a decision. Here there was no time for thinking. The sword
must be drawn instantly or all was lost.

So the downtrodden, suffering poor remained downtrodden and suffering, and expected nothing else. The rich
stayed arrogant and overbearing, and there was no one to
protest. Between them was a gulf so wide and so deep that
no one in his right mind would try to cross it.

When things become too unbearable we usually look for
help, and expect to find it in some leader. It may be a new
President, or king, or leader of religion, but it must be
somebody new and strong and wise, somebody who has our
interests at heart. To such a man we give our support. About
such a man we like to hear stories and to tell them. We
build up around him the kind of good life which we want
him to have.

So back in the sixth century the need rose for help in
lightening the pressure of the unbearable conditions. The
downtrodden come to the point where they realize that
they must have help or go out of existence. When in those
early days a strong chieftain appeared in England, the
people rallied around him, took him into their hearts as their
deliverer, and began as we do, to build up around him
stories of power and magic. This was their tribute to his
defense of them.

This leader was a person of great strength and humanity,
a combination so unusual that it is no wonder the people
loved him. He helped to unite the small kingdoms, and thus
gave them security. He held back the invading Saxons, and
thus gave the Britains time to develop their own culture. He

led them to victories in Europe, and thus made them proud of their strength. Whether his name was Arthur does not matter. Arthur is the name by which we know him.

If it seemed unreasonable later that such a chieftain could have achieved so much success, the story-teller added a little magic to make the story believable. And so as the years rolled by, the wonder at the prowess of Arthur increased. The stories caught the imagination of the people from century to century. Always there has been need of help, always the hope of finding it.

Because there were no printed books back in the fifth and sixth centuries when these events were supposed to have happened, the stories were circulated by telling and by minstrel singing. It is easy to see how the narrator might add a rich detail here and there to heighten the interest of his audience. Such improvements are not limited to the sixth century.

Curiously enough, this way of telling stories seemed to afford a wider circulation than books achieve. All over the world are these stories of the great chieftain, King Arthur, in every language. The French took over the story, and later we have their special line on it, the book of Crestien of Troyes. He added French qualities to the stories but he used Britain for the scenes and the events.

Even out in Turkey I have found traces of the Arthurian legends. Years ago when I was teaching in Constantinople College, an English girl invited me to her home on the Black Sea for Easter holidays. Her father was head of all the life-saving stations on the Black Sea, and she had been born and brought up there. She spoke Turkish like a native, and as

we walked along the shore she often stopped to talk to the
fishermen and boatmen.

One day an old Turk began a long tale. "What is he talking about?" I asked idly. She laughed. "It is an old story he
always loves to tell, and he wants me to tell you."

"What is it about?" I inquired.

"Oh, just about a sword coming up out of the water out
there." She pointed out to water which was so blue that I
thought it should be called the Blue Sea.

She could hardly believe my excitement, but she got the
old man to tell the story and translated it word for word. It
was the King Arthur tale of the arm clothed in white samite
rising out of the water with the gleaming sword in its hand.
It was a King Arthur tale told by an old Turk who could
neither read nor write, and who had never been away from
the shore of the Black Sea.

Where did he get it? Oh, his father, his grandfather, any
good Turk who lived here could tell that story. And he was
much pleased to find somebody who wanted to listen to it.
What invaders, perhaps the Crusaders, had carried the story,
or how it originated, I never knew. But I did know from
that moment how wide and how deep was the distribution
of Arthurian tales.

At last when people began to read and write, the stories
took their place in print. And there they have been ever
since. In the middle of the twelfth century the women especially began to demand romance. By the next century the
romance plots were in full swing. Someone has called the
Arthurian romance the world's first great novel. If the plots
sometimes sounded like fairy tales, their essence reflected the

society of the time. Small wonder, then, as a famous Arthurian scholar has remarked, that you cannot expect consistency in Arthurian romance.

It was the Age of Chivalry which drew its sustenance from the King Arthur tales. Again as time had swung its great arcs of the centuries over the earth, the Middle Ages came along with as downtrodden and suffering poor as ever existed. Conditions were so bad that people looked forward to the destruction of the earth, to the burning of the world and the fall of heaven upon it. It seemed better to die than to live in such torment.

But now in this everlasting rhythm of man's efforts to better himself, the ideals of knighthood began to lighten the darkness. The warring knights took over some responsibility for their vassals. They began to use their strength in the service of the weak and oppressed. They protected women and surrounded them with sentimental ideals which they wove into stories. They started an era of greater consideration for the dignity of the human race.

From the middle of the eleventh century to the end of the fourteenth the Middle Ages struggled to pull itself out of the slime. The King Arthur ideals contributed more help, perhaps, than we can measure. Knighthood became a responsible state not to be undertaken lightly.

The preparation for it began in childhood. At seven the son of a nobleman became a page at some castle or in the court. Until he was fourteen his schooling was all concerned with principles of knighthood, protection of others, obedience to his betters, the truths of religion. Not a bad foundation for youth to grow upon!

Then at fourteen he became a squire, and that meant a

strict training in horsemanship, in how to behave among the knights and ladies, and in the implements of war.

At twenty-one his training was over. With impressive rites he was formally made a knight. His armor and his sword marked him as a man grown, ready to face the troubles of the world. He swore to defend the weak and the poor, to be loyal to the king and the church, to avoid any form of slander, to love and marry one maiden only, and to be true to his own word. Even if no human being in those days could live up to such promises, he had at least taken a step in the right direction.

Through the years came the records of knightly ideals in books, for printing had now become a means of communication. They served to spread more widely the new doctrines of civilization. Geoffrey of Monmouth began with a Latin history of King Arthur which probably few people could read. But it was translated into English and French, and so the foundation was laid in the twelfth century.

From that time on, the stories of King Arthur became part of the heritage of the race. When in 1470 Sir Thomas Malory wrote his classic, LE MORTE D'ARTHUR, he gave the world in permanent form the story of King Arthur and his knights. And to this day, the book is interesting reading. Beneath its archaic style are drama and emotion. Its fine, difficult print blazes with the light of truth. It is art, and history, and beyond everything to people in those dark days, a stimulus to right living. The influence of King Arthur and his knights on the human race is beyond measure.

Modern youth may well ask, "How much of this story can I believe?" For in these days of science we ask for proof of what men say. Yet perhaps these old story-tellers were wiser than they knew. They may have added magic for effect, but they incorporated into it a kind of symbolism which is eternally true.

The sword could be drawn out of the stone by one person only, and that person had to be the right one. Not strength of muscle was necessary, for Arthur was only a boy. But behind his physical effort must lie strength of spirit such as none other possessed. Would that we might always test our leaders by some such magic!

There may not have been a shining silver chalice which had served the Lord's Last Supper and which now could cause miracles to happen. But the Holy Grail serves as the symbol of the aim toward which the pure in heart strive. An end which is not concerned with personal gain, with money or with fame, but with the beauty of the spirit. The churches take it over, and struggling humanity keeps its eyes on the shining goal.

The Round Table itself may be a kind of symbol of unity and equality. It had no head nor foot where the greatest or least must take his seat. These knights sat about a Table Round where each man's place was graven with his name. Just as today each member of the Cabinet has his nameplate on the back of his chair. They could look each other in the eye, and catch each shadow of thought and feeling. Their justice was the product of united effort.

So through these tales of King Arthur runs a lovely symbolism which deepens the interest and adds richness of content as we work it out while we read. And here we have another contribution of King Arthur and his knights to the landmarks of the world.

Read these tales, then, and realize as you read, that here through the most potent magic of all, the power of the printed word to convey reality, you have come upon a might that moved the world.   M.L.R.

KING ARTHUR AND HIS KNIGHTS

1

Boyhood Severed
by a Sword

DOWN ACROSS THE SWEET-SMELLING MOORS THE
two boys raced. The keen air from the sea blew
them along and gave their feet the lightness of
their spirit. The sun beat on their bare heads, and
lent promise of a fair day for the tournament. Arthur's pace quickened until he saw his shadow

reaching past his brother's, and then he held his
steps in sharp discipline. Nothing angered Kay
more than to have Arthur pass him. His age gave
him priority, he held, his dark face glowering at
any sign that it was disputed.

Arthur, who could throw boys bigger and
stronger than Kay, agreed wholly with his brother,
and took great care not to offend him. He had no
fear of him, but he loved him. They had grown up
together with a father who rarely interfered, and
the very freedom of their life gave them rare understanding of each other.

Arthur could not know what deep satisfaction it
gave his older brother to rule without question
such a splendid fair-haired boy. Nor would he have
cared. He had the kind of world he liked to live
in, and he would change nothing in it. A comfortable home, a father, Sir Ector, who let his boys hunt
with him or by themselves, a strong sound body,
and now a chance to see the jousting at the tournament. Again his step quickened so that he almost
stumbled over Kay who had stopped short.

"I've left my sword at home!" Kay cried, his

face dark with anger. "You hurried me so that I forgot it. Now what can I do!"

"I'll get it for you!" Arthur had already wheeled about. "I'll have it and catch up to you before you know it!" He was off with such speed that Kay could not help but realize his superior swiftness.

Off across the moor, now running as fast as he liked, strong in lungs and wind, his fair head like a spot of gold moving through the sun. He was out of sight before Kay could answer, though he would have heard no dissent for now Kay had stretched himself out in the heather to wait Arthur's return.

Back to his home, across the shallow moat, up to the great door, and it was locked. The whole house locked soundly, for the dwellers had gone along with the rest of the countryside to the tournament. Now what! Arthur searched his resources and found nothing.

Yet Kay must have his sword. He would not enter that great gathering place, he, Sir Ector's elder son, without his sword by his side. For a boy like himself a sword did not matter, but Kay would go no farther without his, and Arthur had no wish to lose the tourney. He could not leave Kay alone on the moor, and anyway there was small chance that Kay would make it easy for him to go on without him. Arthur looked away from the cold granite wall out into the golden morning, and felt the profound despair of a disappointed boy.

Suddenly he leaped to his feet from the stone step. What was it he had heard the knights talking about yesterday? A sword! A sword stuck in a stone! Stuck in a stone over by the cathedral. They hadn't been able to pull it out. Arthur felt the smooth hard muscles of his arm under his fingers.

"It would do no harm to try," he said. He flung himself across his horse, which was grazing quietly in the meadow. "I'll pick up Kay's horse on the way back, and then we'll lose no time." He loped off toward the cathedral.

The place was deserted for everyone had ridden away to the tournament, but there in the churchyard Arthur saw a great stone with an anvil of steel rising from it, and in the steel had been thrust a shining sword. Arthur did not hesitate a moment. Here was a sword which even Kay would like. He did not stop to read what the letters in gold said. He seized the handle of the sword with so fierce a grip that he staggered backwards when it came out with such ease. He laughed aloud, tucked the sword under his cloak, and rode off at full speed.

Now the morning was right again. The air was cold on his face as he swept over the moor, Kay's horse following close behind. He lifted his voice and called, "We're coming! We're coming!" though he was not within hearing distance. He had a sword for Kay. Now they could reach the tourney in time. His voice rose like a trumpet through the morning.

Kay heard and leaped to his feet scowling as if he had waited longer than he could bear. Arthur rose in his stirrups, pulled the sword from under his cloak, and held it out to Kay, who looked so astounded that for a moment Arthur was discouraged. But then the older boy seemed to accept his explanation, his dark face filled with a kind of calculating pleasure. He leaped on his horse, and with Arthur following, they raced across the moor. Out of the crowd reaching like rays toward the focus of the gathering place, Kay seemed to search for someone.

Arthur saw him first and called out to Kay, "You see, we got here as quickly as our father." Then he had to turn and follow Kay to Sir Ector's side. But he feared no delay for he knew that Sir Ector was not a knight to miss a tournament.

He sat his horse, idly waiting while Kay showed his father the sword. Not until he heard the words, "Here is the sword of the stone. Now I shall be king of the land," did he straighten to attention. What was Kay talking about!

Sir Ector turned a startled yet penetrating look upon his elder son, wheeled his horse about, and called to the boys, "Come with me." Back across the moor he headed his swift horse, and the boys followed as best they could. Again Arthur's despair darkened the golden morning. Was it by his own hand which had taken the sword that did not belong to him he had lost the tourney? This he could not bear. But still he must follow, and now they rode into the deserted churchyard. Then he, too, leaned from his horse and for the first time read the words written in gold: Whoso pulleth out this sword of this stone and anvil is rightwise king born of all England.

Arthur straightened in horror. Now what have I done? he thought. But he felt relief as he heard Kay with lowered eyes telling his father that he had the sword and therefore was king of the land. Perhaps they could now settle the matter quickly and get back to see the end of the jousting.

But Sir Ector still bent that grave penetrating look upon his son. "Come with me," he commanded, and led them into the cathedral. There he laid Kay's thin dark hand on a great Bible opened for the morning service. "And now, my son," he said in a voice which neither boy had ever heard or would disobey, "swear upon this book how you came by that sword."

At last Kay lifted his eyes. "My brother Arthur brought it to me."

"And you?" The grave look was upon Arthur now. "Where did you get this sword?"

It was not in Arthur to lie or to distort

the truth. He told freely and sorrowfully of how he had borrowed the sword for Kay, and that he had not harmed it because it withdrew so easily. "See, I will put it back where it belongs," he offered, and thrust it into the stone. Now perhaps they could go on. "Nobody was here or I would have asked leave," he explained. "You can see how easily it goes back where it belongs."

Sir Ector's face was unreadable. He turned again to Kay. "Now you shall draw the sword," he said.

Kay pulled until his face was deep red, but the sword did not stir. He flashed an angry glance at Arthur and stepped back, rubbing his arm.

Then Sir Ector stepped up to the stone. "Now watch, Arthur," and he proved to him that however hard he pulled he could not stir the sword. "It is your turn now," he said, and stepped back to make place for Arthur.

The lad could not bear the feeling of suspense. His fair face was crimson to his hair. He would get it over with quickly. "It's easy," he said. "Your hand may have slipped on the handle." He drew

Arthur drew the sword from the block of stone.

the sword as if it were thrust in soft clay, and would have passed it over to his father.

But when he turned, he saw to his horrified embarrassment that his father, and perhaps more incredibly Kay himself, were kneeling on the earth before him. He cried out aloud at the sight. "No! No! What does this mean? Why must you, my dear father and brother, do this thing to me?" He felt he could not bear this incomprehensible end to the promise of the morning.

Sir Ector rose, for after all the situation was as strange to him as to Arthur and he was not used to kneeling. Kay looked uncertain, and rose too. Then Arthur felt more comfortable. But Sir Ector was still not himself. His kindly assurance of authority was gone. He seemed to be feeling his way back into a past where Arthur could not follow.

At last he spoke. "No, Arthur, you are not my son," he said and his words were cold truth in the boy's heart. "Nor is Kay your brother." Kay not his brother whom he willingly followed? Sir Ector not his kindly responsible father on whom he could always depend? Who then was he, a boy without the moorings of a family? What had this sword which he wanted only for Kay done to him? His world was shaken like his heart.

So there they sat in the dark cathedral, the bright day outside forgotten, while Sir Ector with deep sadness at hurting the boy he loved, told Arthur about how he had come to be one of his family. For Arthur such pain was so new and harsh that he could scarcely follow Sir Ector's words. He wanted only that the tale be done with and that they step back into the life which he knew. It could not be himself, young Arthur, who was the child of this tale!

There was much about Merlin, and of Merlin, the magician, Arthur had heard many tales. A man of extraordinary power who believed that he could manage the lives of people better than they knew themselves, who extorted strange promises and deeds from his victims, and who generally saw to it that the outcome was to his own advantage. Could this man Merlin who could change his identity from beggar to knight, who was ruthless in his intentions, could he have touched the happy

sheltered life of a boy like Arthur? It was unbe-
lievable.

Yet it was so, Sir Ector told him with words
that came slowly, heavily, as though he drew
them out of a past which he, too, had wanted to
forget. Merlin had brought the baby to him, a
fair strong boy, and told him that it was written
that he should care for him, a child of noble birth.
Then Sir Ector smiled down into Arthur's anxious
face. "We could never have resisted you, my dear
wife and I, even without the command of Merlin."
And somehow Arthur's heart lifted a little.

So wholly had they taken the child into their
love that his origin never troubled them. He was
as much their own as was Kay. But now—

"But now what has come about?" cried Arthur.
"I am still your son. I could belong to no one else.
Let us forget the sword which has made us all this
trouble, and ride away to the tourney." But somehow the gay holiday was too far away even for
thought, no part now of this strange day. He still
must listen. And finally believe.

"So finally," Sir Ector ended, "this sword has

proved your royal birth. As king I ask of you only the favor that your foster-brother Kay shall be made seneschal of all your lands. I know that you will be my good and gracious lord." His voice had simple confidence.

Then Arthur stood in sudden dignity, tall and fair in the dark cathedral. "If ever I am king," he said, and the possibility seemed far from him, "I will never fail you. You shall have of me whatever you wish. Nor shall anyone but Kay ever be seneschal of the lands," and he was astounded at the gratitude in Kay's eyes. This story still could not be true.

But then Sir Ector led them to the archbishop, and there Arthur heard the tale again, and against his own will began to believe it. The archbishop was a kindly old man who recognized the trouble in the boy's clear blue eyes.

"We will wait a little," he said soothingly. "On Twelfth Day all the barons will be here, and they shall try the sword. If they cannot move it, then Arthur shall try again. Keep your heart light, my son, and God be with you."

But for all his cheer, the boyhood of young Arthur was over, and in some strange way he knew it. The people in his home seemed never to forget the sword. He found his dear mother weeping at times, and could not comfort her. He disliked Kay's humility. Much better the old relationship where Kay tried to rule and Arthur still did as he liked. Now he did not even know what he wanted to do. Nor could his father help him for Arthur could not penetrate that strange respectful attitude. He was impatient for Twelfth Day.

It came, and left behind it many angry barons. For not one had been able even to loosen the sword. And their wrath knew no bounds when a tall straight boy stepped up to it and drew it from the stone with no effort whatever. Never, they said, would they be governed by a young lad not even of royal birth.

So from feast to feast the archbishop postponed the decision. He put knights on guard by the sword night and day. More and more knights arrived to test their strength on the sword. Yet there it stood except when Arthur pulled it out with such ease. At Candlemas they tried, at Easter, until finally the disturbance grew so great that the archbishop would wait no longer. His edict was made public that the matter must be settled at the feast of Pentecost.

The knights gathered from far and near. The archbishop saw to it that knights were near Arthur all the time guarding against trickery. For an honest, outgoing lad who had always been trusted this attitude was one he did not like. By this time, too, he had won for himself a certain pride in his prowess. If he could draw the sword from the stone, and he knew that he could, he did not mind who else knew it. This time he looked forward to the trial, if only to finish all trials. A boy could stand just so much!

At the feast of Pentecost people gathered from all over the country, for the word had spread that every knight should take his turn. Not only the lords and ladies came to the trial but the poor people who were called the commons, so poor that they had nothing of their own. Life had ground them down, but they still liked to watch their betters. They stood in great dark patches outside the limits where the gleaming knights and their lovely ladies gathered. They watched and waited. Nothing had ever come their way to help them yet, but still they hoped.

Then the trial began. Knight after knight rode up to the sword, grasped it with all confidence, put into it his whole might, and left defeated. Each time a murmur like dust rose from the dark patches of the poor people watching outside the circle.

One by one, until the day grew short, and still no knight could stir the sword. Each one rode back and watched the next one try, hoping perhaps that since he could not achieve success no one else should. And no one had stirred the sword even to the last knight who rode away as angry as the rest.

Then the archbishop nodded his head to Arthur, and the boy walked forward, his fair head alight in the setting sun. He stood a moment, tall and straight before the sword, as if thinking of its terrible significance to him. Then he bent forward, pulled lightly, and stood there facing the crowd with the sword swung in his hand.

It was enough for the commons. They had seen the miracle. Here was their lord and master. They burst into a great roar which reached across the moors to the sea. "We will have Arthur for our king and no other," they cried. "We see that God wills it, and we shall slay any who would prevent his rule."

Arthur heard the deep call rolling past him like a command. He turned toward those poor people kneeling now to him, and held toward them his sword. He paid small attention to the knights who were yielding too. From now to the end of his reign he committed himself to be the king and upholder of the poor.

2

The Young King Proves
His Strength

NOW ARTHUR WAS PLUNGED FROM THE FREEDOM
and ease of boyhood into the responsibilities of the
adult. Nor were they the ordinary duties of a man
which must often be taken over by the young who
are unprepared. From a light-hearted boy who ac-
cepted without question the pattern of his life, Ar-

thur now was a king who must decide the pattern
of the lives of his subjects. The leap was a long
one, and it was no wonder if it left him breathless
at times.

But Arthur had a good mind as well as a sound
body. With his coronation he had promised himself that his rule should bring justice to the poor
and downtrodden. If his inexperience made him
unwise sometimes about the means he chose to accomplish his ends, it was no wonder. A boy should
have a chance to grow up gradually.

It was no wonder either that he turned for advice to the man of all the kingdom who made it
his business to give advice. Wherever there was
trouble, there was Merlin, and whether he helped
it or caused it no one was quite prepared to say.
He never hesitated, however, to work his magic in
whatever direction he saw fit. He had a special
hold upon Arthur because he seemed the only one
in the world who knew about his birth. Merlin
was canny enough to keep his secret until Arthur
had begun to depend upon him. With all of the
new and pressing duties of a king, wholly un-

trained for his high place, Arthur was in sore need
of advice at times.

Strong in his intentions toward the downtrodden, Arthur, with the buoyancy and faith of youth,
began to right wrongs, to return lands to their
rightful owners, to make his country the kind of
place which gave him pride. None of these
changes could happen without causing disturbance.
Even in our own day where everybody, old and
young, shares the problems of the world and tries
to solve them, no new way is offered without trouble to accompany it.

When the coronation was over with all its pomp
and glory, Arthur gave a great feast thinking to
make friends with the neighboring kings for in
those days each small country had its own king.
He looked forward greatly to this feast which he
could give himself instead of hanging on the out-
skirts as he had always done.

"I will find a right and beautiful gift for each
king," he told Kay, who was now seneschal of all
his lands and much too busy to attend to presents.
"And lesser gifts for their knights who will come

with them." Good food, comfortable quarters, rich gifts, and an eager young host whose only wish was to make friends with his guests, all the signs seemed right and sure of success.

So glad was King Arthur that the kings and knights were coming to his feast to do honor to him that he sent messengers out to meet them with the gifts which he had chosen. Then he dressed himself in his richest robes for he was young and wanted to make a good impression on his elders. He waited, growing more impatient, until finally the messengers, dejected and weary, came back, and Arthur saw that they still bore his gifts.

"What has happened?" he cried in puzzled anger. "Why have you failed to deliver my gifts?"

For a time they would not speak, but stood before him with bowed heads. Then Arthur felt real alarm. Had there been floods or some barrier in their way? He commanded them to speak, and he spoke as a king. So then they told him.

The kings would have none of his gifts. They gave the messengers harsh treatment and bitter words, and sent them away. Their message to Ar-

Knights and swords and horses were destroyed.

thur was that they had no joy to receive gifts of a
beardless boy of low birth, and that their gift to
him would be hard and sharp swords across the
head and shoulders. For it seemed a great shame to
them that such a boy should rule this wide land,
and they were on their way to take it from him.

Such wrath swept over Arthur then that it made
him forget he ever was glad, or was but a boy
among all these men. And indeed his anger at
their treatment of him may have thrust him over
the boundary of his youth into their own territory.
He was not to be intimidated by them!

He called five hundred armed men together,
and with plenty of good food to keep them contented, he prepared for a siege in a strong tower
nearby. There was no time to be lost, and it took a
clear head to crystallize plans from all of the noise
and confusion about him. It was Arthur's first
real test as a leader and a warrior. And he passed
with honors.

For fifteen days the tower stood the siege, and
then Merlin, who must always identify himself
with trouble, arrived. The kings and knights were

by this time puzzled and discouraged by their lack of success in trapping the lad they despised. They turned upon Merlin with angry questions though they felt relief to find someone who always had the answers to puzzles.

"Just why," they asked him, "was that boy Arthur made your king?"

"Well, my good sirs," said Merlin, pleased to find such a fine opportunity to divulge his secret. "I will tell you why he is our king, and it is a sound reason. His father was King Uther Pendragon, and the throne rightly belongs to his son." He told them how he had delivered the boy to Sir Ector, and ended his long story with a prophecy of Arthur's future success which made the knights wince.

As usual Merlin succeeded in stirring up more trouble for, although these men believed in his supernatural power, they had no mind to accept it this time without question. At last Merlin got them to agree to talk with King Arthur, and then he went into the tower and told his story to him.

"Come out," said Merlin. "Meet them as their

equal and better, talk to them without fear, and
you will see them yield."

Since Arthur could meet them in no other way
because he had no fear and was at heart friendly,
he did as Merlin suggested, and Merlin as usual
got the credit. But the knights would not yield,
the words grew harsher, and finally fighting began.
Somehow men in those days, as well as in these,
seemed to settle a final issue by killing each other.
This is, after all, a terrific block to the advance of
civilization, and seems to settle nothing since new
men are always ready to spring up and fight again.
Even then, with no other method ever considered,
the futility of it seems to have stirred Arthur, and
perhaps served to give birth to his idea of his
Round Table.

Merlin now urged Arthur to fight for his kingdom and for his life, and since Arthur had no
other choice he flung himself into the combat with
everything which he had. Merlin looked on with
pleasure. And to some degree Arthur shared briefly
his pleasure, for three hundred of the best men
with the besieging kings came straight to him and

said that they were with him and would fight for him.

Knights and horses and swords were destroyed until at last the kings had nothing with which to carry on the siege. They took all of their knights who were left alive, and fled. Merlin, seeing that the fight was over, appeared to Arthur and counseled him to follow them no farther. Arthur willingly obeyed since, as in the old days with Kay, he meant to do what he was told anyway.

"Now," said Merlin, "don't think that these kings are going to accept defeat. They will be right back stronger than ever, and you must be ready for them." He then advised Arthur to seek the help of the kings of France and Benwick with the promise that he would in turn help them in time of need. This seemed to insure fighting for a long time, and Merlin was well pleased.

He was right, too, for the fighting continued until so many good knights were killed that it had to cease until they could get fresh supplies. Arthur took part in it all until finally he found himself without a sword. Instantly Merlin was at hand. "I know where one waits you," he said. "Come with me."

They rode along together until they came to a quiet and lovely lake. Here seemed a strange and peaceful spot to find a sword, yet as Arthur looked out over the blue water he saw rising out of the water an arm. The arm was clothed in white samite which gleamed in the sun, and it held erect a shining sword. A girl seemed to be crossing the lake.

Merlin nodded. "The Lady of the Lake," he said. "She lives there within a rock, and if you speak fair to her she will let you have that sword."

The damsel came closer, and Arthur bowed low to her. "What sword is this," he asked gently, "which the white arm holds above the water? I wish that it might be mine for I have no sword now."

Then began the curious bartering that always seemed to go with any transaction connected with Merlin.

"The sword is mine," said the Lady of the Lake, "but you shall have it if you will give me a gift when I ask for it."

Arthur, eager only to protect himself again with a good sword, agreed at once.

"Well," said the Lady, "it is yours. Row out there in yonder barge and take it and the scabbard from the hand. I will ask for my gift when I want it."

Arthur, with the eagerness of youth for its present needs, tied his horse to a tree and with Merlin set out in the boat. When they reached the white arm Arthur leaned from the barge to grasp the handle of the sword. He had no doubts for had he not established himself as king by his earlier handling of a sword? The hand released the sword into Arthur's grasp, and then sank slowly under the water.

Arthur examined his prize with delight. It had a wonderful scabbard which Merlin told him he should like better than the sword for it was worth ten of the sword. But Arthur held to the good sharp sword. His experiences lately had convinced him that no sword could be too strong.

"This sword," Merlin told him, "is Excalibur. Hold to it as long as you have life."

Here was a promise easy to keep, and Arthur rode away to his knights, who greeted him with the friendliness of those who knew that their leader shared all of their dangers no one of which would make him flinch. He might be young, he might be inexperienced compared with some of these old fighters, but he never seemed to lack courage and he was resourceful in an emergency. These the knights knew for valuable qualities.

He was, moreover, either by his honest intentions or his success in carrying them out, rapidly winning over to his side the enemies who had fought him. He was able through his courage and his numbers to withstand foreign invaders who would have liked only too well to annex this rich kingdom. They found that they were mistaken in their idea that it was inadequately protected. Arthur not only knew how to take care of what belonged to him, but he knew how to add to it. He was a good man to stand behind, and like any good leader he did not lack followers.

Nor did he lack enemies even among the followers. Merlin kept him aware of that fact, and when he did not seem sufficiently impressed, Merlin drew a new story out of his inexhaustible pack. Whether Arthur ever agreed to his method of dealing with one of them may or may not be true.

"Now," said Merlin, "I can tell you by my magic that a child born on May-day will when he is grown destroy you. What are you going to do about that?" Quite possibly Arthur had not been asking Merlin's advice often enough of late.

Arthur, somewhat concerned because after all he believed with the rest of his world in Merlin's magic, may have left the matter in his hands. There was never any question about the thoroughness of Merlin's methods.

On pain of death Merlin sent for all babies born on this day. He put them aboard a ship which set out to sea, and of course met with disaster. Out of the wreck one child was cast up and saved by a fisherman. That child was Mordred, and when at the end he was connected with the death of King Arthur, Merlin if he had been alive might well have said, "I told you so!"

At the time a good many lords whose children were sacrified were in bitter distress and anger. But even then they did not blame Arthur, who was no coward in his ways of meeting trouble. Because they were so sure of Merlin's guilt, and because no ordinary man knew how to deal with a man of magic, they held their peace. Even more angry they would have been if they had known that the whole sacrifice was in vain because the one child who would cause trouble had escaped to grow up. The ways of Merlin's magic were not always infallible.

3

Arthur Chooses His Queen

NOW THAT THE BARONS HAD MADE UP THEIR minds to accept Arthur as king they decided that it was time that he had a wife. Arthur had been too busy defending his kingdom and adding to it to have much thought for the ladies. As ever when he was unsure he turned to Merlin.

"These barons will give me no rest," said Arthur, "until I find me a wife. What would be your advice about such a step?"

"A good idea," agreed Merlin, who had without doubt given the matter considerable thought. "A man in your position should certainly have a wife. Have you seen anybody who might please you?"

"Well," said Arthur, who had his mind all made up, "the loveliest lady I know is Guinevere, the daughter of King Leodegrance who has the Round Table. Do you think she might consider me?"

Merlin was not pleased but he knew when he met an insuperable barrier. "She is not the choice I would have made for you," he said, "though she has great beauty, high birth, and riches. I could find you a lady who would bring you greater happiness."

"What more could a man want?" Arthur inquired reasonably. "I will take her or none."

"She will not love you," warned Merlin. "Her heart is already given. There is a knight called Launcelot who has won her love, and will always keep it. But if your heart is set, I know that you will not change its course."

"That is the truth," agreed Arthur, who had no manner of doubt about his skill in outdoing the rival called Launcelot. "Now go on and make the arrangements." And he furnished Merlin with all the men he wanted to make the visit to the father of Guinevere.

King Leodegrance was already favorably disposed toward Arthur because he had come to his help in a time of trouble with his enemies. Then it was that Arthur had first seen Guinevere, whose beauty and grace had won his heart until he could think of no other lady as his wife. She, like almost everybody else, responded to Arthur's friendliness and they had talked and laughed together as young people do. Indeed Arthur did not know that he loved her until back in his home he found her beauty haunting him everywhere he turned. The only way that he could satisfy his restlessness was to make her his Queen when she would always be a part of his life.

Leodegrance was well pleased when Merlin told

him of Arthur's wishes. His daughter could not do better than marry a king like Arthur who gave promise of such greatness, and who for a young man had proved himself the equal of and better than his elders.

"This is the best news that I have ever heard," he told Merlin, and began at once to plan appropriate gifts for so great an honor.

Nobody apparently asked Guinevere how she felt about the matter, but in those days the daughter was a part of her father's property, well-loved perhaps but wholly obedient to his wishes.

"Since Arthur has so many lands," pondered Leodegrance, "I will not give him more. But he shall have as the most worthy gift I can make, the Round Table which his father, King Uther, gave me long ago."

With this table belonged a hundred knights who should go to Arthur, and there were still fifty seats to be filled because so many of the knights had been killed. But Merlin assured the king that he could fill the vacant places.

So off they set, the lovely girl with her attend-

So off they set, the lovely Guinevere and her attendants.

ant ladies, and her regrets, if she had any, well hidden, the hundred knights, and the Round Table. Back to London they traveled where Arthur awaited them with all impatience and delight.

Guinevere was even lovelier than he remembered, and he was sure that out of the whole world he could not have made a wiser choice for his Queen. The Round Table he welcomed more than the gift of any lands. Here were men of wisdom and experience who could help him to carry out plans for the lives of his people. He sent Merlin out at once to find the fifty knights which the Table still needed. Then he threw himself into preparations for the wedding and the coronation of his Queen.

Merlin could find only twenty-eight knights who suited him, but every year at the feast of Pentecost more were to be added as they proved themselves worthy. It was a high goal for the knights. When Arthur called them together Merlin bade them rise to do him honor, and when they stood they saw that each chair had the name of its owner in letters of gold. Only one seat was empty for a long time, the one called the Seat Perilous, because if anyone unworthy should sit there he would be destroyed.

So King Arthur established his great Order of the Round Table which was to last for so long. His knights were sworn in with high ceremony so filled with deep meaning that it must have shaken their very hearts. There they stood taking the vows to honor their knighthood by their loyalty to their King, and by their promise to do no wicked deed while they lived, a difficult promise indeed to keep.

Here they established the ideals of chivalry which were to last so long and which would help lift the downtrodden and the weak to places of safety. Here they would fight for the right, care for the safety of the ladies, resist injustice, be merciful, and always bear themselves with courage. Their ideals were high, and if they failed to reach them all they had the glory and the struggle of their attempt. And they gave a legacy to a world which sorely needed it.

Even in this day youth strives toward those same ideals, and puts them into form and action in the aims of the great scout movement for boys and girls which has swept over the earth. Perhaps when those ideals are really taken over by youth so completely that they become a living part of the adult, our world will live again in the light of peace. It was a hope which Arthur could not even have imagined, but which like a strong truth built the foundation of his Round Table for his knights and for all of us who came later.

Now, as Arthur had promised himself when he drew the sword from the stone, he would care for the poor and the oppressed, and he would see that every man had his chance to live his life as well as he could. It was a high aim which he set himself, and we would do well to strive toward it.

In no way swerved from his Round Table duties by his coming marriage, and perhaps spurred on by the promise of his happiness, Arthur directed the preparations for his wedding. With Guinevere at his side he could accomplish miracles!

She, too, found the stir and pomp exciting enough to forget all else. Though a daughter of a king, she was not used to the magnificence of Ar-

thur's court which was all laid at her feet. It was
not so much to impress Guinevere that Arthur thus
did homage to her, but perhaps to help her to understand the kind of life which stretched ahead of
her. And no girl would but be impressed by such a
future. Guinevere put Launcelot out of her mind,
and she thought out of her heart.

The wedding was held at Camelot and never
had a wedding more pomp and beauty. It is no
wonder that the English people like to see their
royalty married since even now a royal wedding
adds to its solemnity by so much of the formal
splendor of the past. Arthur had planned well,
and all went so smoothly that it must have irked
Merlin.

The magician went to the knights of the Round
Table and told them to sit still, that soon they
would see a strange and marvelous adventure.
They watched, always ready for adventure. Soon a
white hart ran into the hall, pursued by thirty pairs
of black hounds, which seemed an unfair advantage but which pleased Merlin.

Around the Table raced the poor hart, and of

course was bitten by one of the hounds. Perhaps
some knight felt the injustice of the chase, and
tried to stop it, perhaps he was angry because the
hart fell against him and overthrew his seat. Anyway he rose, picked up one of the dogs, and rode
off with it.

On so small a cause could Merlin stir up trouble, for at once trouble began. Arthur was glad to
have the dogs gone for they made so much noise,
but Merlin told him that he could not dismiss such
an affair lightly. He advised Arthur to send for
Sir Gawaine, Arthur's nephew, who had just been
knighted, and to make him go after the white hart.
Out of this incident and the order from Merlin
arose such a series of fights that even Merlin must
have been satisfied.

Sir Gawaine, feeling his oats at this first chance
to prove his knighthood, managed in his zeal to
kill by mistake the lady of the knight who owned
the hart. Such disgrace was this deed that when
Gawaine got back Guinevere organized a jury of
ladies to try him. They condemned him and ordered that he should always for his whole life fight

the quarrels of the ladies and nothing else. A punishment out of proportion to his sin!

The white hart, moreover, was killed in the turmoil, and so in the end no one was bettered by the slaughter, which is quite likely to be true of this method of settling difficulties. For when Sir Gawaine withdrew from the chase, another knight, Sir Tor, took it up, and after him came still others. On the whole, enough trouble was started to please even Merlin.

Now Arthur's Court was complete with its Order of the Round Table, and with his Queen whom he dearly loved. His knights might go about seeking adventure which usually was incomplete unless someone was slain. But Arthur had matters of great import and far reach to settle. His country must be defended from invaders like the Saracens, and it must be added unto by his skill in invading. He dealt with large adventures indeed, and his success grew with his experience.

Merlin, who was growing old, did not figure so largely in his decisions, which may have been one reason for their success. Curiously enough, it was one of the ladies who brought about Merlin's downfall. He fell in love, himself, and to show his prowess he taught the lady his ways of magic.

When she had learned all that she could of Merlin, she put upon him one of his own enchantments. He had shown her a great rock which was wrought by magic, and she persuaded him to go under it with her so that she might show him how successfully she had learned her lessons from him. So successful was she that she wrought his own magic upon him and imprisoned him in the rock. None of his incantations helped him now, and the lady went away and left him in the rock.

And that was the end of Merlin, without whom Arthur may have been much better off.

4

Arthur's Favorite Knight, Sir Launcelot

THE COURT OF KING ARTHUR NUMBERED SO MANY knights who followed the same pattern of adventure that only a man of superior quality could stand out among them. Among the knights whose names are known because of their achievements and valor is Sir Launcelot.

49

Because he loved Guinevere to the end of his days he became a symbol of romantic love. Because he suffered so many of the sorrows and the penalties which such a love was bound to bring he won the sympathy of the ages who have read about him. As a knight he was strong in combat; as a lover he yielded always to his love.

Next to King Arthur, himself, Launcelot had most renown among the knights. No project of his ever seemed to fail. When Arthur had any special task of great difficulty he would turn it over to Launcelot. Always they were friends, and Arthur would believe no wrong of Launcelot.

His achievements in battle did not lessen his charm for Guinevere. From her high state as Queen she felt free to distribute her favors as she willed, and Launcelot was not forgotten. Nor was he forgotten by the other ladies. For this knight, besides the attraction of his courage, had that quality which belongs to few people and is rated high because it is so rare, the quality of charm.

All his life the ladies swept after him begging his favors. He was loyal indeed that under all this pressure he managed to stay faithful to his love for Guinevere. Some of the stories had it that the pair had drunk of the potion which Merlin had meant for Arthur to secure Guinevere's love for him, and that the magic of that potion would never let its victims go. More likely, the young pair fell in love with each other during those early days of Launcelot's visit to her home, and the very impossibility of marriage made the romance take on beauty to them.

So Launcelot was always harried by the ladies who saw him with all of his grace and power unattached to any one of them. On one occasion he was pursued by four of them at once. They came upon him in a group, and each in her turn told him how she loved him.

These four queens found Launcelot asleep in a wood. Morgan le Fay, who was Arthur's sister and who stopped at nothing to get what she wanted, put an enchantment upon him and the four bore him off to her castle. There, when he woke up, they gave him his choice of the four. They told him that they knew he loved Guinevere but that since he could not have her, he must choose one of them, or else die in this prison.

Launcelot may have felt quite rightly that this was no way to win a man's heart. "This is a hard case," he told them, "that I must make a choice of death or one of you. But on the whole I'd rather die than have one of you attached to my life. As for lady Guinevere I could prove to you that she is true to her lord Arthur."

"Is this your final answer?" they asked.

"It is," said Launcelot. "On my life you are all refused."

They went away, probably somewhat puzzled, and left Launcelot much dejected but still firm. He was hungry, and when at noon a fair damsel brought him some dinner he received her with his usual charm. She at once told him that if he would but do as she said she would get him out of this trouble with no disgrace to himself.

He promptly agreed without asking her what she wanted, which seemed to be the way in those days. Whereupon she asked for help for her father, and since Launcelot knew him he readily promised.

Sir Launcelot was King Arthur's favorite knight.

Early the next morning the damsel came and led
Launcelot through twelve locked doors to his horse
and armor, and off he went after an affectionate
and grateful farewell to the damsel. When he
reached the house of the king who was her father
he found her there waiting for him, and he could
not have been too greatly surprised. But from
now on, Launcelot had no attention for anything
except the combats into which his promise had
plunged him.

Indeed, they needed all of his attention. Knight
after knight waited his turn to kill the renowned
Launcelot. But they had no luck. He left behind
him tales of valor and dead bodies wherever he
went. Now and then he varied his efforts by rescu-
ing some fair maiden who usually hoped to win
his love. He always told her that he would have
none of the state of wedlock, and went his way.
On the whole he seemed to enjoy his special kind
of life very much.

One night he came through a deep forest to the
castle of Tintagil in Cornwall. The village people
all gave him warning but he rode on to the court-

yard. There he found four knights who set upon him, but he promptly killed two of them and the other two ran away.

There after a good night's sleep he found Sir Kay, who was trying to fight his way free from three knights. Launcelot, refusing all help from Kay, struck down the three knights with six of his strokes. Then he set free threescore ladies who had been imprisoned and forced to work on silk garments to earn their food.

Before Launcelot left, he exchanged horses and armor with Kay unbeknown to Kay, and went out thus disguised to fight Kay's battles successfully. When he finally rode away, the knights he left alive looked at each other and said, "Who is he?"

"Well," said one of them, "he is certainly a man of great might. I wager my head that it is Sir Launcelot. I know it by the way he fights, and the way he rides."

Thus had his reputation preceded him. And since this adventure was a typical one of his days, the knight made a safe guess.

Launcelot had a keen eye for danger, too, which

served him well. Once he came upon a castle
where he could see fluttering and struggling a falcon. The bird could not free itself and Launcelot
was sorry for its plight. When a lady came out of
the castle and called to him for help he went readily to the rescue of the bird. The lady helped him
to take off his armor, and he climbed up to the
falcon.

Then, just as the lady held the hawk safely in
her hand, the knight who was her husband,
armed and with a sword, rushed out of the woods
and stood at the foot of the tree to slay Launcelot.

Angry at the treachery which had betrayed him,
Launcelot broke off a great branch, leaped out of
the tree, and gave the knight such a blow on the
side of the head that he fell down. Then Launcelot took the knight's own sword and cut his head
off.

When the lady mourned because he had slain
her husband, he told her quite reasonably that
they had meant to slay him through falsehood, and
that now the punishment had fallen upon them
both. Then he put on his armor, mounted his

horse, and rode off through the woods for more adventures.

Two days before the feast of Pentecost Sir Launcelot got home. He chose his time well when there was a great gathering of lords and ladies. When he rode into the Court in Sir Kay's armor, and told his story, there was much laughter at the way his plan worked. And much admiration for his other exploits.

Then Sir Kay arrived and told how he had ridden in perfect peace because Sir Launcelot had left him his horse and armor so that no one dared attack him. Then the Court heard all about the four queens and Launcelot's escape from them, which must have delighted the ladies' hearts. Altogether he had built up for himself a record of success which made him the greatest knight of his time. Everywhere he was received with honors, and not the least to pay him homage were the ladies.

Yet all of this homage could not save poor Launcelot from trouble, and the trouble came, as might be expected, from a lady. Guinevere quarreled with him, violently and without much reason, as people who are under a strain so often do. She called him a traitor and told him that he was never to appear at her court again.

Launcelot was so heartbroken that he acted like a madman. He fell to the floor, then he leaped out of the window into the garden and fled. And where he went no one knew. Guinevere, repent ant, wept and wrung her hands. She ordered a search for him, and gave her own treasure to pay the knights. But no one could find him.

Quite out of his mind, Launcelot wandered through the woods living on berries and fruit for three months. If anyone came near him he hurled himself at the intruder with such force that he never came back. When he came to a town the boys chased him and threw stones at him. When some knights guessed that he might be a person of note they built him a little hut with straw, and threw meat inside because they dared not go near him.

Finally, as usual, a lady came to his help. The

daughter of King Pelles found him asleep in her garden and went for some knights, who carried him to a tower where the vessel called the Holy Grail was hidden. Beside this vessel, which had its power because it served the Lord's Last Supper, they laid the sleeping Launcelot, and when he awoke he was well. Though for a fortnight he still had to rest because he was stiff and sore.

When he finally returned to Arthur's Court there was great rejoicing, and none rejoiced more than Guinevere, who had been the cause of all this madness. Whether she learned a lesson or not would make a great difference in the end of Launcelot's life.

But now Sir Launcelot was strong in mind and body again. He was back in King Arthur's Court where he felt himself at home. The King himself was his warm friend. The Queen had made amends and now offered him her loving care. Within and without the Court all paid him homage. The stars shone high for Launcelot at this time.

5

Tristram

AMONG THE KNIGHTS WITHOUT NUMBER WHO lived in Arthur's Court the name of Tristram takes a high place beside that of Launcelot. He was quite a different person in character and in his whole way of living. He was gentle and kind in his youth and would have liked very well to spend his days

in quiet pursuits like hunting and hawking which
he studied with great care. But no knight in those
days could deliver himself over to peaceful pursuits. His whole reputation depended upon his abil-
ity to fight.

Nowadays a man can gain some fame in other
directions, and if Tristram had lived in later times
he might well have been a famous ornithologist
like Audubon, or a biologist like Agassiz. Who is
to say what the world might have gained if he had?
Even in those days he managed to make such careful notes of his observations and discoveries that
the terms he used still do service for hawking
and hunting. And the book of such sports is called
the Book of Sir Tristram.

Tristram, like so many of the knights, was the
son of a king. Meliodas, who was lord of Lio-
nesse, was his father, and his mother was a lovely
lady, Elizabeth, who was sister of King Mark of
Cornwall. So this boy had royal heritage.

Yet his name, Tristram, came to him through
his sad birth. His father had been taken prisoner

while hunting by a spiteful lady who wanted him for herself. The women in those days went out for anything they wanted!

When poor Queen Elizabeth missed her husband she was heartsick with worry. She took one of her ladies with her and ran into the woods to search for him. The cold and the fear shook her heart so that she died there in the forest. Before she died she asked to have her baby called Tristram, which meant sorrowful birth.

As so often happens the sacrifice was needless. The king escaped the next morning and came home to find his wife dead, and a little child on his hands. He had indeed cause to mourn.

Yet until Tristram was seven years old he had the kind of life he liked best. His father saw that he had good care, and the boy roamed afield with the birds and animals as freely as he wished.

Then King Meliodas decided to take another wife, and he did not choose as well this time. The new queen was jealous of Tristram because he would have the kingdom instead of her own sons.

So, with the usual direct method of the ladies, she tried to poison Tristram. Fortunately for the lad one of her own sons drank the potion.

This death, however, did not discourage her. She mixed another potion and set it out. The king, who was thirsty, saw the cup and picked it up. Then, only, did she reveal her plan. She snatched the cup from him, and when he threatened her with his sword she told him the truth about how it was meant for his son, Tristram.

She was condemned to be burned as a traitress, and the fire was made ready for her. But the gentle-hearted boy could not bear this tragic end for his stepmother, and begged her life of his father.

The king finally consented, and said, "You may do as you like with her but I will have none of her." Nor would he, though Tristram tried to make peace between them. But the stepmother felt only gratitude and love for Tristram always, which was a comfort.

Yet now the king would no longer have Tristram around, feeling it impossible, probably, to understand such forgiveness. He hunted up a tutor for the boy and sent him off to France. Here Tristram learned a new art which he mastered and loved. He became a skilful harpist and was known far and wide for his beautiful music, a rare achievement which must have taken a dauntless spirit in those days.

Living there in France with his tutor, Tristram grew into a strong and handsome youth. He had captured a certain kind of happiness for himself and at nineteen he must have been a boy of whom his mother would have been proud. It was a pity that he could not hold to that happiness through his adult life. He returned to Cornwall, and his father discovered that he had a son who pleased him greatly.

At once Tristram was plunged into warfare. Of his own accord he offered to defend Cornwall from Sir Marhaus who threatened it. He begged his uncle, King Mark, to make a knight of him, and then he set forth.

Sir Marhaus felt uncomfortable about attacking so young and inexperienced a youth, but Tristram would not listen to him, and soon the two men were fighting fiercely. To the surprise of Marhaus, the lad remained fresh and strong though he, himself, became winded. Finally Marhaus fell down on his knees and Tristram thrust his sword through his head. No surgeons could cure him, though they found a broken piece of sword in his head, and from his wound Sir Marhaus died.

Tristram, himself, was badly wounded, and could not seem to recover, until at last a wise woman said that he must go to the country from which the poison on the tip of Marhaus' sword came. There he might find help. So Sir Tristram took his harp and sailed off to Ireland. Even in his stress he did not forget his harp.

Knowing well that he would not be welcome in the country which was the home of Marhaus, he did not give his own name but called himself Tramtrist. So much better did he feel when he arrived in green Ireland that he sat up in bed and played his harp with his lovely light touch. Never had the people heard such music, and they welcomed the one who could make it.

The good King Anguish had a daughter called the Fair Isoud because of her beauty and her grace. Though so young and fair she still had a kind of special wisdom which made her a skilful surgeon. The king turned over to her his suffering guest, Tramtrist, and she practiced upon him all her skill. With such a nurse and doctor to make him well, Tristram would have been grateful. But here was the loveliest lady he had ever seen as well as one who was kind and wise. The splendid young pair had no choice but to fall in love.

Those days were so full of happiness that they could not hold enough hours for Tristram and Isoud. He played his harp to her, and then he taught her to play it, loving her light awkward touches on its strings, and guiding the white fingers. Then she obeyed him, but when he tired she took charge and made him rest. And so with their love growing stronger every day the two young people lived in a world of their own, bright as the sun with their happiness.

Then one day when the queen mother and Isoud were in Tristram's room the queen picked up his

sword and noticed the piece broken from it. She
ran to her chamber where she got the broken piece
which was taken from the head of her dead
brother, Sir Marhaus. The piece fitted into Tristram's sword and seizing it she ran to kill this false
guest, Tramtrist.

A knight prevented her, but she demanded Tristram's death of King Anguish in no uncertain
terms. The king said sternly, "Leave this matter to
me to settle," and sent for Tristram. When the
young knight told him frankly who he was and
what he had done, the king was greatly distressed.
He saw that Tristram had fought for Cornwall,
and that what he did was honorable for him.

"But now," said the king, "I cannot keep you in
my country with honor to myself. You must go."

Tristram thanked the king for all that he had
done, and begged to say farewell to his daughter.
Poor Isoud wept bitterly when she knew that he
must go for she loved him dearly.

"I promise you," vowed Tristram, "that I shall
be your knight as long as I live."

"And I," said Isoud, "promise you that I will

not be married for seven years without your consent."

Each gave the other a ring to seal their promises, and Isoud wept as if her heart would break. For indeed the crash of all her happiness was hard to bear. When he took his harp and went away from her he carried with him the light which had made her days the brightest she had ever known.

Tristram said farewell to the knights and ladies of the court and sailed away to Cornwall, and never again in his life was he to know the clear young delight of his love with Isoud the Fair. She was always in his mind and like any young man he talked constantly of her to King Mark and his court where Tristram now lived.

At last the uncle, King Mark, who was a coward and jealous of his handsome young nephew, gave to him the order that he should go to Ireland and demand Isoud for Mark's queen. It is hard to understand the lad's obedience, but custom and relations were strict so that Tristram felt that he must obey or disgrace his knighthood which King Mark had given him.

The good King Anguish was delighted to see Tristram again, believing that he had come for his daughter, Isoud. To Isoud the whole world was right again, and the days moved as swiftly as the beat of her heart.

The shock was hard to bear when Tristram revealed to them that he had come for Isoud at his uncle Mark's command. "But I would rather have her marry you," King Anguish said. And Isoud looked at him with terror in her lovely eyes.

But there was no choice, and the pair set off on a ship for King Mark's court. The two must have wished that the voyage would never end. Again like Launcelot and Guinevere, they were supposed to have drunk of a love potion in the cabin one night, and after that they could never love anyone else. But Tristram and the Fair Isoud had already given their love to each other such honor and strength that they needed no potion. As long as they lived, they belonged to each other.

For Tristram there was no comfort. When his dear love was married to King Mark, he, like Launcelot, lost his mind for a while and wandered in the woods. He had done his duty as a knight to the best of his belief, but his sensitive spirit was wounded and torn.

Queen Isoud had little pleasure in her high state. When a cousin who wanted Tristram's estate started a rumor of his death, Isoud herself nearly died of sorrow. When finally some knights brought the mad man of the woods to the castle he was so changed that she did not know him.

But no matter how a man may look, his dog will know him. When the little dog which Tristram had given Isoud caught his scent, he leaped upon him with whines and cries of delight. Nor would he leave his side. Then Isoud knew that Tristram was alive and here, and she could hardly bear the tide of happiness which swept over her.

King Mark watched the dog and knew, too, that Tristram had returned. He tried to make his barons condemn Sir Tristram to death, but they refused, and would only consent to his banishment for ten years. He set sail leaving word that he would return when he could. King Mark must have felt uneasy at this message.

At once Tristram was plunged into the high adventures of knighthood. He saved a knight who was unfairly attacked by two barons, and found that it was King Arthur, who was indeed grateful. He fought for hours with another knight, and when neither would yield, he discovered that it was Sir Launcelot he had happened upon. Then each knight proffered his sword to the other and there was peace and good feeling between them.

Back at Court King Arthur and Queen Guinevere gave Tristram a warm welcome, and Arthur offered him his highest honor, a seat at the Round Table. When they looked they saw that the seat which had had the name of Sir Marhaus on it was now named Sir Tristram. So Tristram became an honored member of King Arthur's Round Table.

King Mark was as jealous as Queen Isoud was glad that Tristram was so honored. By trickery Mark managed to get Tristram back to his castle, though it may not have been too difficult with Isoud there awaiting him. Mark broke his promises to Arthur of good behavior, and thrust Tristram into prison at the first opportunity. When

King Mark slipped in carrying his sword.

Isoud knew that he was in prison in her own
court she could have died of grief.

But Tristram had stood all of the tyranny and
treason from King Mark that he meant to bear.
When a gentle person is roused, he works with
good intent. He wrote a letter to Isoud asking her
to be his lady for always, and that if she would,
she must without King Mark's knowledge get a
ship ready for them to sail to England where they
would be safe.

Isoud, too, had borne trouble too long. When
the letter came, she roused from her grief and
made ready to depart. She put her good mind to
work on the problem and in a short time had
Mark in prison until she could release Tristram
and sail away. There could not have been a voyage
of greater joy than this crossing to England of the
pair who had waited for each other so long. No
matter what happened later, they had now a few
years together, and after the long time of suffering this was enough.

Launcelot took them to his own castle, Joyous
Gard, and commanded his people to love them and

to honor them as they did himself. For three years Tristram and Isoud lived together in such happiness as is not often given to anyone. If it seemed a short time, it had after all a kind of perfection which made it complete, and more than that they could not ask of life.

They sat together with their little dog one evening while Tristram played his harp to Isoud. The music now had sharp ecstasy which it had never known. They had indeed nothing more to ask of life, and life was through with them. For such happiness is not made to live forever.

King Mark, treacherous as always and now jealous beyond endurance, slipped into the room behind Tristram and thrust his sword through his brave nephew's heart. In one short moment a great life and love were finished. And though all who were concerned with the treachery were punished by death, life could not be brought back to the dead.

For Isoud, having found her happiness, could not see it depart. When she saw that Tristram was beyond her help and could live no longer, she fell unconscious upon his body, and died before she woke again to her sorrow.

Here beyond all the other knights was one who stood for loyalty and faith. He had much sorrow in his life, for he was well named, but he won a kind of happiness from it which, like his music, was higher and sweeter than the world had yet known.

He loved well, he fought well though often against his will, and he had, beyond the desire to kill, an ever deepening desire to know how live things live, and to help them to do it. He was a creative person rather than a destructive one, and what he created lives long after him.

6

Galahad

IN ALL THIS TIME THE SEAT AT KING ARTHUR'S
Round Table marked Siege Perilous had not been
filled. No knight dared claim it because of the
promise of destruction if he were not the right
one. Somewhere King Arthur was sure there must
be a knight who could win this seat in safety. And

he hoped that he would come soon, for the years
were passing.

He was right. Far away from the Court in a
quiet cloistered castle a boy was growing up. Here
he lived in peace with the nuns who gave to him
generously all of their wisdom and understanding.
Here he spent his youth in the security of their
love and of the goodness of the God they worshipped. Here he lived without the companionship of other boys but well content with the life
which he had.

He was a boy of great beauty and strength with
a noble bearing which seemed to indicate high an-
cestry. But the nuns had taught him well that he
was a child of God, and he had little curiosity
about his human relations. "Keep your heart pure,"
they told him, "for the pure of heart shall inherit
the earth." The child, Galahad, tried to live in the
ways they taught him.

These nuns knew well that the beautiful boy
for whom they cared so tenderly was the son of Sir
Launcelot and Elaine, the daughter of King Pelles.
But it was not for his noble birth they cherished

him. Galahad was a lovable boy. When it came
time for the nuns to deliver him over to his rightful life they felt deep sorrow. But he was reaching
manhood and he must have his chance with other
men.

Twelve of the nuns went forth with him, and
though it was a sorry trip for them, the young
Galahad must have been filled with high excitement and curiosity about the new ways that
stretched ahead of him.

In the great valley below the abbey of the nuns
they came upon Sir Launcelot who had been bid-
den to ride there. The twelve nuns stood in a half
circle with their boy in their midst.

"Sir Launcelot," they told him, "we have nour-
ished this child to manhood as best we could. Now
you must make him a knight."

Launcelot saw the beauty and the promise of the
lad, and felt his heart go out to him. "Does he,
himself, wish to be made knight?" he asked.

The nuns and Galahad spoke together, "Yes."

They left their boy, and the abbey must have
seemed a lonely place without him, and Sir

Launcelot made Galahad a knight. Launcelot left
the young knight to take care of himself while he
went back to Camelot for the feast of Pentecost.
The great hall was empty until the knights returned from church service, and Launcelot wandered about the room looking at the names on the
seats.

On the Siege Perilous which every man had
avoided he found fresh letters written in gold
which said that four hundred and fifty winters
after the death of Christ this seat should be filled.
Launcelot counted the years and realized that the
time was now. The knights were greatly excited,
and covered the chair with a silken cloth until it
should be claimed.

It was a custom at Pentecost that they should
not eat until there had been some sort of adventure. They stood waiting until a squire came in
and told them that at the river was a great red
stone floating with a sword stuck in it. The King
and the knights all hurried to the river, and at the
King's bidding some of them tried to pull it out.
It would not move, but they were satisfied that

they had had their adventure and went back for their dinner.

Then suddenly the doors and windows of the hall closed though a strange soft light filled it from within. The knights sat still in great suspense, watching, waiting. While they sat there still as death, an old man clothed all in white entered the room. Behind him was a beautiful young knight with an empty scabbard by his side.

The old man led the young knight around the table to the seat beside Sir Launcelot which was labeled Siege Perilous. He lifted the silk cloth and the letters read now: "This is the siege of Galahad, the high prince."

"Here is your place," the old man said, and went away.

When Galahad took his seat safely, the knights all did him honor because they knew that he had been chosen above them.

Then King Arthur showed Galahad the stone in the river, and told him that the other knights had tried and failed.

Galahad put his hand on the sword and drew it

lightly from the stone. He put it in his empty
sheath, and the knights all saw that here was one
who would surpass them all. King Arthur watched
and remembered that even so in the earlier days
he had drawn his own sword. He knew the test
had proved Galahad's right to this perilous seat
which only he could occupy in safety. He
welcomed the lad to the order of his Knights of
the Round Table.

But such a knight must earn his welcome. For
Galahad the peace and quiet of the nuns in their
abbey were over. Ahead of him now was the
need to prove his worth. As if it had been part
of his birthright he found himself gifted with skill
at jousting and in the tourney. He knew no fear
of an adversary, and usually vanquished him.
His success was hard for the older, more experi-
enced knights to bear, but it gave Galahad confidence that he could handle his new life.

Beyond and above every desire in a knight's
heart was the wish to find the Holy Grail, that
heavenly vessel which had disappeared after the

Lord's Last Supper. It was known that to none but the pure in heart could such a vision be granted. Yet ever since Galahad had come to the King Arthur Court there had been strange reminders that the Holy Grail was near them. The room would become luminous with a lovely light, it would be filled with rare scent. The very air was charged with the mystery and beauty of something which no one could see.

When at last the knights could no longer stand the suspense Sir Gawaine spoke for them. "I make this vow," he said, "that tomorrow morning I will start on a quest of the Holy Grail. I will search for a year or more if need be, but I shall not return until I have seen the Holy Vessel."

At once the other knights rose to follow him for they had been only waiting for the word to start. King Arthur was dismayed because he realized that nevermore would they be together, and he could not bear to be bereft of his noble companions of the Round Table. The Queen and the ladies wept, but nothing could turn the knights from their resolve. Even the reminder that only the one who was clean of sin should succeed had no effect upon them.

The next morning after the church service the King took count of the knights who were leaving him, and found that there were one hundred and fifty, every knight of the Round Table. The King wept when he saw them go, for with them went his high hopes for his Round Table.

Each knight chose his own way to go. Young Galahad had no shield, and so for four days he rode along cautiously. Finally he came to a white abbey where he found two of the other knights. They told him that here in this abbey was a shield which no one could bear unless he could prove himself the most worthy knight in the world.

One of the two knights tried to wear the shield and barely escaped with his life when he fought with a White Knight. "Take this shield to Galahad," the White Knight commanded. "He is fit to wear it."

When Galahad had put on his shield and rid-

den a way he came upon a hermitage and found
the White Knight there waiting for him. The
Knight told Galahad the story of the shield, which
Joseph of Arimathea had marked with a cross of
his own blood. He had ordered that no one should
bear the shield until Galahad claimed it because
he was the last of Joseph's line.

When the Knight had given his order he vanished, and Galahad could not tell where he went.
The lad rode his horse slowly back to the abbey
while he thought about the responsibilities which
had been so suddenly loaded upon his young shoulders. But they were strong shoulders, and he held
them straight and sturdy as he rode into the future.

In that future were many adventures which
would test all of Sir Galahad's endurance. When
he chose as friend to ride with him, another
young knight called Melias, the trouble began.
Young Melias insisted upon taking the fork of the
road which was plainly marked dangerous for anyone who was not without sin. He saw a crown of
gold and tried to ride away with it. At once a

knight rode after him, and wounded him so that he lay upon the ground as if he were dead.

When Galahad, hearing the cries, rode through the woods to help his friend, the knight set upon him, too. But small chance did he have against Galahad's sword and shield. Galahad drove him away, and rode back to take his friend to the abbey where a good monk would care for him until he was well.

Then Galahad rode on until he came to the Castle of Maidens. It was a strong castle by the river Severn, and it was surrounded by deep ditches. An old man warned him back from it. He went straight on until he came upon seven knights prepared to defend the castle. Then Galahad set upon them with his wonderful sword until they ran through the castle and away by another gate.

Now the old man held out the keys to Galahad and he opened the gates. Inside he found in the halls so many people that he could not count them. They were waiting to welcome him because they had been imprisoned for so long by the seven wicked knights. Here many maidens had been

killed and the poor people had been robbed of all
that they had.

One of the maidens brought Galahad a horn of
rich ivory to call some of the other Round Table
knights to his help. He blew the horn and the
sound reached through the woods for miles. The
knights heard it and hurried to its call. Then with
Galahad to direct them they set free all whom the
wicked knights had held in bondage.

The next morning one of them told Galahad
that they had killed all of the seven knights. "That
is good news," said Galahad, and buckled on his
armor and rode away.

Over and over again the brave young knight
came upon strange and dangerous adventures. Always he rode away the victor. His courage which
never failed him served him even better than his
shield and sword. Ever he watched for the downtrodden and those who were hurt. Never did he
leave them until he had helped them.

Once only he ran away, and for that hasty departure no one could blame him. Two knights had
set upon him, and with the complete disguise of

armor he had no way of knowing who they were. He had unsaddled both of the men, and had broken their swords to their great astonishment.

Nearby was a hermitage, and just as Galahad was getting ready to run his sword into the knights, he heard a voice from it say, "If those two knights had known you as well as I do, they would let you alone."

Sir Galahad had no wish to be known, and he may well have recognized his father by this time. He put the spurs into his horse and galloped off like the wind. Though Launcelot and his friend rode after him as fast as they could, young Galahad was out of sight in no time. They shook their heads and let him go.

Neither the father nor the son could have regretted this hasty departure. For once caution was the better part of valor!

Yet all these adventures did not seem to Galahad to bring him nearer to the great goal toward which he was striving. He had learned how to conduct himself as a knight. He had saved lives, and taken them. He had kept himself pure in heart in the days when such a quality was so rare. If he could once find the Holy Grail, he thought, he would ask nothing more of his life. Young as he was, he had no wish to live beyond that great moment.

At last one day as Galahad rode through a deep forest he came upon a hermitage and went in to rest. The old hermit was glad to see such a fine young knight, and gave him some of his scanty store of food. While Galahad rested quietly a loud knock sounded on the door. The hermit opened it and outside was a gentlewoman who said that she wished to speak with a knight called Galahad. So the hermit woke Galahad and sent him to the door.

"Galahad," she said to him, "you must now mount your horse and follow me, and I will show you the greatest adventure a knight ever saw."

Galahad forgot his weariness and rode after the woman. They rode fast until they came to the sea, and there they found a ship which seemed to be waiting for them. The woman left him, and Galahad went aboard where he found his good friends,

Bors and Percival, who gave him warm welcome. They set sail with a strong wind, and Galahad was glad of the sea and of the companionship of friends.

At last they came to a castle, and when Galahad entered he was swept by the feeling that now he was nearing the end of his search for the Holy Grail. True enough, as they sat there alone in the hall they saw a vision in which angels prayed about a table of silver. The Holy Vessel stood there and while they watched a voice explained to them that though they had glimpsed the Grail they must go to Sarras to see it fully. Here the people had come upon such evil ways that the Holy Vessel could no longer stay with them.

Back to the ship went the three knights and sailed again, eager to reach their goal. After they had sailed three days they woke on a clear morning to see the city of Sarras before them. On board with them was the silver table and the Holy Vessel covered with red samite.

When they landed, Galahad called to an old man to help carry the heavy table.

"But I can't," the old man cried. "I have been a cripple for ten years."

"Never mind," said Galahad. "Get up and try to lift your share."

The cripple obeyed, and to his amazement he found that he was as sound and well as he ever was. He took his end of the table opposite Galahad, and carried it easily.

The king of Sarras was a tyrant and he objected so much to all of the honor which the knights received that he threw them into prison. Yet while they were there the Holy Grail cared for them so that they did not suffer. And at the end of a year the king died and the whole city rose and chose Galahad for their king.

Here was as high an honor as the people could bestow, and one that showed how much they appreciated the quality of the young knight. Yet it was not the life for Galahad, and he was glad when it came to an end.

At last the year was over, and in it Galahad had done many good deeds for these people who had trusted him to be their king. Then one morning a man called him and told him that he was Joseph of Arimathea, and that now he would show to Galahad the full marvel of the Holy Grail.

Galahad trembled with fear and with rapture. At last his life was to be fulfilled, and he was ready for its completion. For to him to go on after this high purpose had been achieved was impossible. For this glory he had lived, and for it he would die.

Joseph of Arimathea said to him, "Our Lord has sent me here to bear you fellowship because you have resembled me in two things. You have seen the wonders of the Holy Grail, and you have been all your life a knight who has led a pure life." He offered the sacrament to Galahad who received it as his own.

Then Galahad called his two friends, Bors and Percival, and said good-bye to them. And as they watched, they thought that they saw angels lift his soul in their gentle hands and carry it safely away through the bright air. They wept even though they knew that he wanted to go.

Then Galahad saw the full marvel of the Holy Grail.

They saw, too, a hand reaching down through the clear morning to take the Holy Vessel safely away. For without Galahad there was no one worthy to guard it. They watched it go, and felt relief because they knew that they were not fitted to care for it. And since that time no man has dared say that he has seen the Holy Grail.

But from the loss of Galahad the two knights could not recover. He was their good friend and they missed him sorely. Sir Percival entered a holy hermitage where he stayed through his life. Sir Bors returned to King Arthur's Court in Camelot where he told his tale to such effect that the King had it inscribed by clerks and put into a book which was safely sealed into a chest in Salisbury.

The high adventure was over, but the story lasts through the ages.

7

The Fair Maid of Astolat

ALL OF HIS LIFE SIR LAUNCELOT HAD DEPENDED upon his charm, his high spirit, his strength, to give him anything he wanted. He had won great renown from his success in the use of his sword. The ladies had always loved him, and sought his favor, which of course pleased him. Yet Guinevere had his real love, and she still kept him in her heart. Among the knights of the Round Table he was counted first.

But now Launcelot for the first time felt a strange dissatisfaction with himself and his way of life. The favors he received were not enough. They began to seem slight, unimportant. His way of spending his days was the way of a boy, not a man. He felt deep discontent with himself.

All through the Court ran the talk about the Holy Grail, and all about Launcelot men were dedicating themselves to the search for it. He had never wanted anything except for himself and to prove his value to Queen Guinevere. Yet these knights were ready to give their lives for a religious idea.

Even this disturbance might not have stirred Launcelot to action if he had not lived close to his son, Galahad, for a while. Here was a boy who belonged to him, and Launcelot loved him dearly. Before Galahad went away on his final search, he and Launcelot lived on board a ship together for several months. There they learned to know each other, and to realize each other's hopes and beliefs.

Launcelot watched his son thoughtfully. The lad had all of his own charm and beauty and strength, but he did not live to exploit it. His mind and heart were like clear running water in their purity. He had no knowledge of the interests around which his father's life had centered. To hold his attention Launcelot had to take over his son's interests.

The quiet intimacy of shipboard would allow no secrets between them. Launcelot listened to Galahad until at last he, too, longed to see the Holy Grail, to feel its blessing over his life. Finally after the months of peace Galahad knew that it was time for him to go on with his search.

It was a sorrowful parting because they were both sure that they would never see each other again. When Galahad had left, Launcelot sailed on alone for more than a month. In his loneliness he thought always of his son and of the search to which he had dedicated his life.

At last Launcelot saw a castle and it seemed to

him that a voice told him to go into it and he
might see the Holy Grail himself. He suddenly
found that this was the thing he wanted most in
life, and in great excitement he hurried to the
gate of the castle.

He felt free to enter although he knew well
that only those without sin were allowed to see
the Grail. He had talked with a hermit even before
he set sail with Galahad, and confessed that all his
life he had loved the queen who belonged to
Arthur. The hermit had absolved him when he
swore that he would never come into her life
again. He made Launcelot realize that all of his
deeds which had brought him honor were done for
the sake of Guinevere, and not because they were
right and good.

So sure he was that his course was now right
that he was astonished when a dwarf struck his
sword out of his hand and called him a man of
evil faith. But Launcelot was not easily daunted,
and he went on until he came to the door of a
room which was filled with clear light.

As he was about to enter, a voice said to him,

"Do not enter this room for if you do you will repent it."

But Launcelot had caught a glimpse of the table
of silver and the Holy Vessel covered with red
samite. All his life he had done as he wished. He ran
into the room and up to the silver table. And there
he found a power greater than himself, for he was
struck down as if by lightning. He could not stir,
but he faintly realized that hands had lifted him
and carried him out of the room. They put him
on a bed, and there he lay as if he were dead for
twenty-four days. When he finally opened his eyes
he realized that he was well again, and he made
up his mind that the twenty-four days were punishment for his twenty-four years of sin. More than
ever he was sure that he would sin no more.

The holy men told him then that he would
never see the Holy Grail more clearly than he had
now seen it. After this experience Launcelot was
quite willing to believe them. The search was not
for him, and he left the castle to go back to Arthur's Court.

Now that the quest for the Holy Grail had been

fulfilled by Galahad all the knights who survived
the search returned to the Round Table. King Arthur and Queen Guinevere gave them warm greet-
ing. Especially they were glad to see Launcelot,
who at once forgot the promise he made never to
see the Queen again. Gossip stirred in the court
but he paid no heed. Indeed, he was quite his old
self again, ready to joust and full of charm for the
ladies.

As usual one of them fell in love with him.
When he went to the old baron of Astolat to bor-
row a shield, the daughter, Elaine, who was known
as the Fair Maid of Astolat, lost her heart to him
completely.

"Will you," she asked him, "wear this red
sleeve of mine as your token at the joust?"

"Well," said Launcelot, "that is more than I
ever did for any lady, but I shall be in disguise
and none of my friends will know me. Give it to
me."

Unfortunately the jousting was so violent that
Launcelot was badly hurt, and cared little about
who knew that he had a red sleeve for a token.

When Elaine heard that he was wounded she mounted her horse and rode to nurse him. But by this time the Court knew about the owner of the red sleeve, and Queen Guinevere was in a great fury because Launcelot had worn any token except hers.

So the trouble began for poor young Elaine as it had for all the ladies who had loved Sir Launcelot. He could no more help responding to their love than a green tree to the sun, but he meant them no harm. As soon as Launcelot could be moved, Elaine took him back to Astolat where her father, the old baron, and her brother, gave him warm welcome.

Everything was done to make Launcelot comfortable and happy, and without doubt he was both. The lovely Elaine watched over him, and gave him any help she could discover to make him well. Yet when he really was well, she was filled with sorrow because now he must go.

She was so torn by her grief that she told him she would die if he left her. He was her first and only love, and she could not live without him.

Launcelot listened as to a story that he had heard
many times before, and could not wholly believe.
She was so lovely and so distraught that he pitied
her and told her that when she married he would
give her a thousand pounds yearly, a promise
which gave her small comfort. Yet she could not
move him from his love for Queen Guinevere, and
she had to let him go back to the Court where all
the knights and Guinevere waited to give him
warm welcome.

But at last Sir Launcelot's charm had done
harm which time could not repair. The Fair Maid
of Astolat would not be comforted. She neither
ate nor slept for ten days, mourning because he
had left her. Then still lovely, but fragile as a
shadow, she made ready to leave the life which
now held such unhappiness for her.

She sent a message to Sir Launcelot, and her
brother wrote the words for her as she spoke them.
She told him of her love for him, and asked him
to bury her and to pray for her soul. Then she
asked her father to see that she was dressed in her
richest clothes, and with the letter in her right

Elaine watched over Launcelot to make him comfortable.

hand, be put on a barge covered with black samite. A single boatman should steer the barge down
the Thames to London. Then she died, and they
did as she wished.

Down the long dark river the stately barge
floated with the boatman at the rudder but steered
as if by Elaine's own hand. After a while it
found its way under the window of the palace
where King Arthur looked out with Guinevere.
When they saw the black barge they wondered
greatly what it could be, but had no inkling that
it might touch them. Yet the King was curious
and he sent three knights who found the lovely
Elaine lying dead in the barge.

Then Arthur led Guinevere to the barge, and
at once she saw the letter in Elaine's right hand.
When the letter was read they all wept for the
young girl who had given her life for her love.
They sent for Launcelot and read the letter to him.
The Queen watched his face as they read.

Launcelot, who had a tender heart, grieved at
what had happened. But to the King he explained
that he really was not willingly the cause of her

death. "She was fair and good," he said, "and she helped me to get well of my wounds. But she loved me as I did not deserve or desire." He was so honest in his regret that they all believed him.

So then Launcelot did as Elaine had wished, and gave her a rich burial. And he willingly forgave Guinevere because she had suspected him of wrongdoing. Indeed, he had no wish to wrong anybody. Nor was he ever aware of the harm he had done until it was too late.

Now the winter's hunting and tournaments were at hand, and as ever Launcelot flung himself into them with his usual success. His promise to stay away from Guinevere was forgotten, and so, too, probably was the Fair Maid of Astolat who had given her life in vain. Launcelot was absorbed as always in the feats of knighthood and in their effect upon Guinevere. He forgot the words of the hermit who had told him that a man who had such strength and beauty and wit should turn his power in the direction of good. It was enough for him to win applause, and to realize the pleasure which it gave the Queen.

8

Let No One Laugh
at Launcelot

WHEN THE CHRISTMAS SEASON WAS OVER KING
Arthur planned the greatest tournament of all for
Candlemas Day. Launcelot by this time had had
so many honors heaped upon him that he re-
fused to take part in any but a great tournament.
The Candlemas celebration suited him exactly.

Guinevere was pleased too. She called Launcelot to her and said, "I should like to have you wear my token on your helmet. It is a sleeve of gold, and for my sake you should win honor with it." She may have been thinking of poor young Elaine who had given him her red sleeve.

Launcelot took the token and bowed low. "I shall do all that you wish," he promised. Nothing could have given him more pleasure.

Then instead of practicing jousts with the other knights, Launcelot decided to prepare for the tourney by taking a rest. He was a good sleeper and quite frequently in his life took a nap just before or after a crisis.

This time he found a quiet hermitage in the forest. In the woods he discovered a bubbling spring, and every day he would lie still beside it watching it until he fell asleep. He was resting and at ease to make himself ready for the tournament ahead of him.

Unfortunately a lady who was a great huntress lived in the forest and one day, chasing a deer, she shot an arrow into Launcelot by mistake. For once the tables were turned and a woman had done Launcelot injury. She asked his pardon, telling him that she was used to hunting in her forest and had not seen him lying asleep near the deer. But Launcelot was filled with fury and told her that the devil had made her a shooter. She left him then, probably the only woman who saw in him no charm.

Somehow Launcelot got himself back to the hermitage, but he had lost much blood and was in a sorry state. He mourned loudly to the hermit about his bad luck just when he was about to gain such high honor.

"But," said Launcelot, "you must get this arrow's head out of my thigh and make me well. For I am going into the jousts at Candlemas Day no matter what happens." And he meant it.

So everyone, including Launcelot himself, got to work on the healing of his wound before Candlemas Day. And when that day came he rode off as if nothing had ever happened to him. But he must have watched the forest paths to see that no lady huntress was near.

This tournament surpassed any other in its splendor. King Arthur, himself, attended with two hundred of his best knights. The Queen and some of the old knights were judges. As if everyone had been waiting to show his skill, the barons rushed into the jousting with such fury that Arthur could no longer be a spectator. He dashed into the lists with his followers after him, and by himself threw four knights to the earth.

Each knight urged himself on to gain honor, and for a while Launcelot stood and watched. Then like a tornado he raced down the field, smiting to the ground knight after knight. No one could resist him. All of his resting and healing stood him well, and he fought all the day long.

At last Arthur could not bear to see any more of his knights outdone by Launcelot, and he sounded the call to supper in his lodging. There the knights relaxed and had a great feast while Launcelot told them about how the lady hunter had shot him. Then they gave him greater honor than ever, and from Guinevere came highest praise

This tournament surpassed any other in splendor.

of all. No outcome could have pleased Launcelot better.

For Guinevere, too, life was at a high peak. Launcelot was near at hand when she wanted him; Arthur was by her side, trusting, loyal; she was queen of her people and of the two men she loved best in the world. The winter, filled with the excitements of tournaments, hurried past, and spring was on the way. When May comes to England it brings soft air, and bird song, and bright flowers in the grass. Guinevere grew suddenly restless under the pressure of court life. All of her youth gave quick response to the young growing life of spring.

"Come," she cried to her ladies. "We must go a-Maying!" And no one refused to listen.

On this May morning Guinevere would have nothing to remind her of the winter jousts. She would take with her the ladies and her own ten knights but they must all be dressed in green like the new leaves, and no more armed than the trees themselves. They rode forth in the lovely morning to pick their flowers in the meadows with no more thought of the demands of court life than children. The Queen blew about in the bright sunshine like one of her flowers, and all through the woods and fields her lords and ladies scattered as lightly as their own laughter. They had caught the early morning when everything is most alive because Guinevere had promised Arthur to return by ten o'clock. To Launcelot she said nothing, knowing well that he would have no interest in games without danger or arms.

But this kind of occasion with no men of arms was exactly what another knight, Sir Meliagrance, was looking for. He had been in love with the Queen for a long time, but he was so afraid of Sir Launcelot that he had been most cautious. Now he felt that the time was safe, and he would strike.

He rode out into the lovely May morning ready to kill the unarmed knights who might try to protect their Queen. With twenty armed men and a hundred archers he felt fairly safe.

But the Queen had a kind of royal courage which filled her with fury toward this coward. She tossed her flowers into the grass, and drove at him with words sharper than steel. If he had had shame in him, he would have felt it now, but he was not turned from his course, even when she told him that she would rather cut her throat than go with him.

Instead he drove his men into the unarmed knights, wounding them so badly that Guinevere could not bear their pain. She agreed to go with him to his castle provided her wounded knights might stay with her. He consented because he was afraid that left alone one of them might get word to Sir Launcelot of whom he had good reason now to be afraid.

But he had not reckoned on Guinevere's pluck, perhaps because he did not know what courage was, himself. She watched her chance to get word with a young page, and giving him her ring and a message to Sir Launcelot to save her, she sent him off at full speed.

Sir Meliagrance saw the page and shot at him but the boy escaped and found Sir Launcelot. In breathless detail the lad told Launcelot about his Queen's danger, and how her knights who would have protected her had been slain. And probably that young page would never again see a man filled with such fury.

"I would have given all France to have been there well armed!" Launcelot cried, and with all speed proceeded to get himself there well armed. He even made his horse swim across the Thames, and then rode him at a hard gallop until he came to the place where Guinevere had been captured.

Here thirty archers sent out by Meliagrance shot at his horse and killed it. Horses had a hard time in those days! Meliagrance had ordered the archers not to shoot Launcelot for he had a kind of superstitious fear that he could not escape the consequences. And he may have decided that without a horse, Launcelot could get no nearer to him.

But Launcelot's anger drove him on foot through the marshes and ditches where his slow progress became unendurable. Yet he dared not leave his heavy armor because of treachery ahead. Just then he saw a cart which the carter was filling with wood.

"Oh, carter!" he called. "How much will you take to drive me the two miles to a castle?"

"Keep out of my cart," the carter growled. "I am getting wood for my lord, Sir Meliagrance."

He had given his orders to the wrong man this time for Launcelot promptly killed him, and drove off with the other carter who was scared into submission. It was not the way that Launcelot would have chosen to make his rescue of Guinevere, but it got him to the castle.

The Queen was looking out of a bay window of the castle when the cart thundered into the yard with Launcelot swaying at its pace. When she recognized him she knew that he must have been hard pressed to enter in a cart.

But there was no time to wonder for his voice rang through the castle demanding the traitor, Meliagrance. Launcelot leaped out of the cart, burst open the gate, and knocked down the porter.

By this time Meliagrance knew what was in store for him, and he ran in great haste to the Queen, falling on his knees and begging her to save him from Launcelot. Tired of all the noise, and relieved that the danger was over, the Queen nodded assent if he would only keep quiet.

Then she and her ladies went down to greet Sir

Launcelot, and to tell him that the trouble was over.

"Madam," said Launcelot with icy anger, "you may well believe that I would never have come to your rescue if I had known how easily you would make friends with this traitor."

But Guinevere would have none of that. "You know well," she told him, "that I made peace with him to keep him quiet, not because I favored him."

Launcelot, bitterly disappointed that he could not kill Meliagrance, came near to quarreling with his Queen. He gathered together her wounded knights, and the men all complained that they could not be revenged. But the Queen was firm, and so they left Meliagrance alive in his castle.

The adventure which might have been a source of laughter in the Court became through the telling of Launcelot another proof of his indomitable courage. Even the ride in the cart gave him a new title, Chevalier of the Cart, which he wore with pride and thus gave it honor.

As for Guinevere, she no longer cared to go a-Maying.

9

The Cost of a Queen's Life

INDEED, THE QUEEN HAD OTHER THINGS TO THINK about in the month of May which was no longer lovely for her. In that bright meadow filled with flowers she had left her own bright youth. She could look back and wonder that she could have been so light-hearted and carefree. She might long for that high peak of her life again but she could not approach its clear untroubled height.

Even to Launcelot, who welcomed discord as a trumpet calling him to his armor and sword, the days were darkened by a new kind of trouble which had never beset him and which disturbed him. The Court was filled with gossip about his friendship with Guinevere though it had gone on so long without criticism. Launcelot found gossip a kind of slime that the sword could not cut. And Guinevere found it more destructive than any of the dangers which had threatened her young life.

So beautiful and so high-hearted a lady must have enemies, and Guinevere did not lack them in two nephews of King Arthur who hated her. Sir Mordred and Sir Agravaine, knowing well that in their two swords was not as much power for harm as in their vipers' tongues, started tales about the Court which slandered their Queen and Launcelot. They knew well that the loyal King would be hard to convince, but here and there, as is the way with gossip, they spread their tales of slander where they might get back to King Arthur.

Finally when they considered the time was ripe they went together to King Arthur and told him openly that his Queen and Sir Launcelot were a disgrace to his Court in their love for each other. Arthur, angered at the accusations toward those he loved so dearly, yet with his loyalty somehow shaken by the whispers of gossip, demanded proof that Launcelot was not the good knight he believed him to be.

This proof Sir Mordred had carefully arranged. He contrived a hunt for King Arthur, and then on some pretext induced Guinevere to send for Launcelot. His friends tried to persuade him not to go, but Launcelot scorned their warnings. If his Queen needed him, he must as a true knight attend her call. He went straight to the castle where the trap was set for him.

Here the armed knights awaited him ready to take advantage of his unarmed state. But Launcelot, as ever, knew no fear. He tried to comfort Guinevere who was filled with horror because he would be slain, and she, herself, would be burned as punishment.

Well as she knew her good knight, she saw him now with new strength and fire for he was fighting for his Queen. He took her in his arms and kissed her. "Never since King Arthur made me knight have I failed you," he told her. "If I am slain my good friends will save you from fire. But I shall sell my life dearly," he promised.

At times it looked as if he must indeed sell it for there were many armed knights against him. But they should have known that Launcelot was now in his element. All of his strength, and skill, and fearlessness, stood by him. He slew Agravaine with most of the other knights, and succeeded in wounding the evil-tongued Mordred, who ran for his life.

Yet when Mordred reached the honest King Arthur he told such a tale of Sir Launcelot's disloyalty and destruction of his knights that the King believed him. Believed him, and was heartbroken because he must. Now the King knew that his Round Table was broken forever because the knights would be divided in their loyalty toward him and Launcelot. And his Queen whom he had loved and trusted must be put to death by fire. For King Arthur the black clouds of tragedy darkened his whole world.

He had ruled his country with wisdom which not only defended it from outside invaders but built up strength and good living within its borders. Honest and outright himself as a boy, he had grown into an honest and outright King who trusted people as he expected them to trust him. He had not lived his life as King without knowing traitors, but he did not look for disloyalty from his Queen and his friend, Launcelot. Though his heart was broken, he still must obey the mandates of court life and deal out punishment.

But though he knew Launcelot so well, he had not reckoned on the indomitable quality of his courage. If Guinevere died at the stake the tragedy would come to pass only because Launcelot was dead, too. And Launcelot was very much alive.

With the strength that was like an army he charged down upon the crowd which stood around the place where their Queen was to be burned. The spectators fled and they did well to get out of the way. But the knights who were in charge of the ghastly punishment lunged at Launcelot before he could reach the terrified queen. As well try to stop a tornado! Launcelot rushed among them, striking right and left, until he reached the Queen's side. The dead lay on both sides of his path.

He seized the Queen, and with a great swoop of his arm lifted her behind him on his horse. She clung close to him with courage of her own in spite of her fear, and they swept off through the woods with no one to follow them. So they rode together toward safety, together at last, with no one to separate them. Perhaps, after all, Guinevere was not through with high moments in her life.

There was but one place that seemed right for them as they fled. Once Tristram had taken his Isoud to the safety and delight of the castle, Joyous Gard, and here Launcelot would hide and defend his Queen. When the castle gates closed behind them, peace and safety comforted their hearts.

Joyous Gard was a strong fortress which King Mark had entered only by stealth. Now Launcelot strengthened its defenses. For he knew well that King Arthur must uphold his knightly honor.

It happened that Sir Launcelot in his maddened haste to reach his Queen struck down and killed the two brothers of his friend, Sir Gawaine. Sir Gawaine, who had defended the rescue of Guinevere, now joined forces with King Arthur against Launcelot. And so the trouble grew.

For King Arthur there was nothing but sorrow in this revenge which he must take. Yet he had no choice, for Launcelot had killed his best knights and carried away his wife. He gathered together all of the knights who had remained loyal to him. But well he knew that the days of his Round Table were over, and he mourned for their passing.

Launcelot in his castle, Joyous Gard, summoned all of the knights who still believed in him, and were loyal to him. They were many in number and great in strength. The stakes were high; there could be no mercy on either side.

Now more than ever came the proof that no problem was ever settled by fighting over it. The losing side must always try again and again until it is vanquished. And then it will withdraw to strengthen itself for another effort. The killing of men must go on until both sides are too weakened to continue. Nor can peace smooth the way toward good living while resentment and desire for revenge fill men's hearts.

Launcelot, in spite of his skill and valor in war, must have felt the hopelessness and waste of fighting his good friend, King Arthur. Yet there seemed no way to confer with him about the tragic problem which they both faced. According to the custom they must gather their knights together and set them at each other.

Launcelot gathered his loyal knights, but then he staffed his castle with all kinds of good food and made ready for a siege. He would not leave the gates himself, nor allow his knights to venture out. King Arthur and Sir Gawaine with their followers laid siege to Joyous Gard.

At last Launcelot, who found it hard to remain

quiet, went to a tower in his walls and called down to Arthur and Gawaine.

"Let us end this siege. You both know that if I should choose to come out with my knights I could soon end this war. But God forbid that I should make war against my King whom I honor."

"Enough of talking!" cried King Arthur. "I am no longer your King for you have done me deep wrong. You have killed two of my knights who were your good friends, and you have carried away my Queen. Come down here and face me if you dare!"

Then Launcelot tried to explain how sorry he was that he had accidentally killed the knights, and that Guinevere was loyal to Arthur and ready to go with him if he would come for her.

It is not surprising that Arthur might have doubted Guinevere's affection after his ruling about the fire. And Sir Gawaine would have none of his explanation of the deaths of his brothers. The two stood together and demanded battle.

The battle began the next morning. Launcelot had no choice now but to open his gates and march out with his knights whom he warned against any harm to the King or Gawaine. It was an evenly matched battle, and a terrible one.

The King, maddened by sorrow and pain, used all of his skill to kill Launcelot, who fended him off and would not wound him. When Sir Bors would have slain Arthur, Launcelot stopped him. He lifted Arthur to his horse and sent him on his way, bidding him to stop this warfare.

Arthur was deeply moved, and saw Launcelot through tears, mourning that the war had ever begun. Yet he could not seem to end it. When the dead and wounded were taken care of, the battle went on.

So heavy was the fighting, and so great the death toll, that finally the Pope heard about it and interfered. And who shall say that both sides were not relieved at his verdict. A verdict which might well have been reached at the beginning without the terrible slaughter.

Two commands the Pope gave, one that Arthur take his Queen back, and the other that there should be peace between him and Launcelot.

Both of these commands were hard to obey, but the Pope's word was final. Launcelot sent word to Arthur that in eight days he would deliver his Queen to him. Though Sir Gawaine objected, the King withdrew his forces and both sides buried their dead and cared for their wounded.

Launcelot made careful preparation for his final scene with King Arthur and the Court. He was no humble suppliant for favor. As ever, he depended upon the charm of his personality to make his exit unforgettable. He gathered together one hundred knights and clothed them in green velvet with their horses dressed to their heels. Each knight carried an olive branch in his hand as a token of peace.

With Queen Guinevere rode twenty-four of her ladies all robed as the knights in green velvet. Sir Launcelot with twelve young knights paced his horse beside her. Jewels bedecked everybody, even the horses, and the procession glittered in the sun as it marched. But most beautiful and regal of all were Launcelot and his Queen who were both clothed in white cloth of gold tissue, and when the

sun rested on them it did not move except to follow them.

So, too, did the eyes of all beholders who stood
and watched them ride by on their way from Joyous Gard to Carlisle. Many men wept to see bright
romance pass by to its end. It was the kind of
splendid exit which only Launcelot could have
planned and carried through so that the world
would remember its flawless end.

So they drew near to King Arthur who sat still
in his seat with Sir Gawaine next to him to recall
the need for revenge, and the King said not one
word.

Undaunted, Launcelot dismounted and led the
Queen by the arm to her King. Then they both
knelt before him. All the knights wept, and Arthur
looking down on those two bowed heads wept too.
It was Launcelot's great moment.

He rose, and in direct, moving words he spoke
to the King. He told him that he had no choice
but to save the Queen from fire as he had always
tried to serve her. He reminded him of the many
battles he had fought for him, and the victories he

had won for him. He gave him back his Queen and swore to her loyalty.

Sir Gawaine listened with black looks. Whatever the decision of King Arthur, he refused to give up revenge for the death of his brothers. Launcelot offered to do penance. He would not listen. Finally Gawaine spoke.

"My uncle, the King, must accept his Queen because the Pope bade him. But we have agreed together before you came that you cannot stay longer in this country. At the end of fifteen days you are to leave forever. If it were not for the Pope's command I would kill you now with my own hands. You are banished with the King's consent, but wherever I find you I shall yet destroy you."

Sir Launcelot knew that the word was final, but he was not cowed. Though it seemed as if his heart would break, he spoke through his tears. He bade the Court which he had loved so much farewell forever, and every knight and lady, except Sir Gawaine, wept and mourned.

He drew Guinevere gently to him and kissed her good-bye. "If you are ever beset by false tongues, or your loyalty questioned, know that I will deliver you from your danger."

Then he led her by the hand to King Arthur where the two tall splendid figures in their white cloth of gold stood together in immovable sorrow. He left her, and rode away out of the Court forever. His horse paced slowly to the sound of deep mourning, but Launcelot's head was bowed and he turned neither right nor left. Incredibly he was banished, and when he rode back to Joyous Gard he called it ever after Dolorous Gard.

10

A Hard and Cruel Siege

SIR LAUNCELOT RODE BACK TO HIS CASTLE, HIS
mind and his heart so bewildered by his banishment that for the first time in his life he could not
see what he was to do. He had lost everything, he,
Launcelot, who was unused to loss. His Queen

whom he loved he had given back to Arthur. His good friend, Arthur, was never again to be his friend. The Court where he had lived in honor and praise was closed to him forever. What had he left?

The splendid moment when he had stood before the Court with his Queen and shared their sorrow at his renunciation was over. He was alone now, perhaps for the first time in his life, and he did not know where to turn. He, the honored knight, could not bear the shame and banishment. Forever that stigma would be attached to his name which had always belonged in high places. He could not bear it.

He called his knights together and told them that he must go away from his country and leave them. Then Launcelot got such a tribute from them that he need never fear again either loneliness or banishment.

They all spoke at once in such loud acclaim that the walls of the castle rang. "We are with you forever," they cried. "If you wish to stay here we will support you. If you go, we go with you. The fellowship of the Round Table is broken now. In this realm will be nothing but strife. For it was through your nobleness that we had any quiet and peace."

And Sir Launcelot was comforted.

One hundred good knights offered him their strength and support, and Launcelot was so moved that he divided up among them all of his lands in France where they were going, and his riches. What were they to him except something to be shared by those who still loved him? They all worked together packing their goods for departure, and after a while as was usual with Sir Launcelot, sorrow and shame were driven away by the excitement and anticipation which always attended his doings.

He and his knights sailed from Cardiff to France where Launcelot and his nephews had their large holdings of property. They sailed away from their own country to foreign shores, yet they went with pride and determination. For Launcelot the shame of banishment was replaced by high hopes of the future, and his knights shared his expectations.

For them all, the future was more important
than the past.

The people in France who had heard how King
Arthur helped the poor and downtrodden greeted
Launcelot with joy. He distributed food and comfort to them, and gave them work. From King Arthur he had learned what his people needed, and
how to supply their needs.

His knights worked with him, and they worked
so well that he gave them high rank. He called a
parliament, and there he advanced and crowned
these noble knights who had left their country for
his sake. They were busy and contented as men are
when they work for the needs of others.

Yet Launcelot was always aware of future danger. His life in the Court of King Arthur had
taught him the instability of peace. He stocked
his castles well with food and comforts of living.
In case of siege his men should not suffer want.
And Launcelot knew well that Sir Gawaine would
never be content to leave him in a prosperous
state. Banishment was not supposed to raise a
man's rank.

Launcelot was right. Before long King Arthur and Sir Gawaine were ready to sail from Cardiff with many thousand men. The King himself might well have forgiven Launcelot, his old friend. But behind him was his nephew, Gawaine, who never ceased to prod him for revenge. Under his implacable anger at the death of his brothers was probably deep jealousy of Launcelot, a man who could win by his charm and distinction the rewards for which Gawaine worked so hard.

King Arthur's great army sailed to destroy Launcelot. To make sure that England and his Queen would be safe while he was gone, Arthur had made Sir Mordred chief ruler, and in complete power.

When the fleet bore down upon the lands of Launcelot he called his knights together and they discussed how they should treat these invaders who were destroying their towns.

Launcelot listened to their pleas for vengeance. "I am loth to shed Christian blood," he told them. "Let us send a messenger to the King and ask for peace."

"The King would gladly grant peace," they told him. "But Sir Gawaine will not suffer him. He it is who demands your death."

But Launcelot persisted, and sent to Arthur a maid attended by a dwarf asking King Arthur to stop warring on his lands. To give such a dangerous errand to a girl and a dwarf might seem heartless except that such messengers would be the only kind to escape attack. They rode in safety to Arthur's pavilion where Sir Lucan met them.

"Your errand is useless," he told her. "The King would gladly make peace with Sir Launcelot whom we all love, but Sir Gawaine will not let him."

Sir Lucan was right. Though King Arthur was sick with sorrow he could not yield under the taunts of his nephew. Gawaine had a curious power over the older man, who now through his disappointments and unhappiness was shaken in his spirit. In his confusion at the loss of those he loved he could not strike back at Gawaine.

So the maid turned away, bearing Arthur's refusal to retreat. Launcelot wept with sorrow at what lay ahead of him to do to his friend. But his knights said, "What nonsense! It is time that these intruders were driven away. We are better knights than they are, and we ask only to prove our strength to them."

Launcelot, unless he would be considered a coward, had to agree. But he made his followers promise not to attack King Arthur himself. That life so dear to him must be spared.

At dawn the next day the siege began. And it lasted half a year. These knights were too well matched for peace. Sir Gawaine, alone, killed many of Launcelot's best knights. Sure of himself and his power, he finally demanded a chance to fight Launcelot, calling him a coward and traitor.

So then Sir Launcelot called out from his tower to King Arthur that he could endure the ordeal no longer. Now he must defend himself as a beast driven to bay. Sir Gawaine, fearing danger in the King's feeling about his good knight, called out to Launcelot to stop his babbling and come down to the field of battle.

Now Sir Gawaine had a curious power which

he declared a holy man had given him. For three hours until noon his strength increased, but after noon he had to depend upon his own power. Launcelot soon realized why Gawaine stopped fighting at noon, and drove him on until he easily felled him.

Twice this happened, and each time Launcelot refused to kill the wounded man. Instead of feeling gratitude Gawaine still called him a traitor knight. Sick from his wounds for a month he was all ready to fight Launcelot again when strange and startling news came from England which made King Arthur and all of his knights forget their quarrel with Launcelot.

They gathered their forces together and with all the haste that their ships could make they sailed back to England. A far greater danger threatened them now than anything connected with Sir Launcelot. Their own realm was in peril.

11

Mordred, the Usurper

BACK IN ENGLAND SIR MORDRED HAD BEEN LEFT
in charge of the kingdom, and he liked it. He had
no mind to give it back to his uncle, King Arthur.
He liked the power in his hands, and he fell under
the charm of Queen Guinevere as many a man had

done. He decided that he would keep both England and Guinevere for his own.

He wrote letters which were supposed to come from abroad and which announced that King Arthur had been slain. He called together a parliament and made it choose him king. He was crowned at Canterbury where he held a great feast and received much acclaim, for the people always enjoyed feasts and somebody new to talk about.

Then, feeling very much a king, Mordred announced to Guinevere that he intended to marry her. He set the day for the wedding, and he gave Guinevere no choice. She listened to him with a heavy heart which she hid from him.

But Guinevere had more than once outwitted suitors who would have carried her off. She allowed Mordred to make his pompous demands, and then she asked his consent to one small favor. For such an important occasion she must, of course, have new clothes. Surely he would want her to look her best! And with that, she looked at him the very best she knew how.

It was enough. Mordred consented, and off to

London went Guinevere. Not to the shops she went, but straight to the Tower of London which she took over for her own. In great haste she ordered her followers to fill it with good food and plenty of the supplies for living. Then she entered with her knights and quietly but securely shut herself up in the Tower.

When Mordred heard how she had duped him he was filled with fury. He had tasted his power with relish, and he had no mind to let a woman get any of it away from him. He rushed down to London and laid terrific siege to the Tower. He was sure that no woman could resist this noise and danger.

But Guinevere stayed in her Tower, and sent word to Mordred that never for fair words or foul would she trust herself to him again. She would far rather kill herself than be married to him. Her words did nothing to soothe him, and he flung his forces against the Tower with all of his fury.

Then the Bishop of Canterbury tried to dissuade Mordred by threatening to curse him with bell, book and candle.

"Go away!" Mordred commanded him, "or I will strike off your head."

The Bishop went. And seeing trouble ahead, he withdrew into the safety of Glastonbury. So now Guinevere had no help.

By this time the news that Mordred had taken over his kingdom and his Queen had reached Arthur, and Mordred heard that he was on his way home to avenge himself. It was time to take action with the people. He left Guinevere in her Tower, and gathered together the knights of the kingdom who favored him.

There were plenty of these knights to join him. In those days, even as now, people soon tired of one man and of one way of living. In spite of all the benefits of King Arthur's reign they were quite ready to join another ruler, hoping for better things with newer ways. Mordred collected a strong host to go down to Dover to meet King Arthur.

The great navy of ships sailed into the slaughter from Mordred's men. But now Arthur was his old self again, filled with courage, and anger at evil. He drove into Mordred's army and soon had it in flight. His spirits rose with his success, but not for long.

In one of the boats he found Sir Gawaine lying more than half dead. Here was a blow greater than he could bear. He bent over the still form in deep sorrow.

"Ah, Gawaine, must you leave me too? What have I left in the world? In Launcelot and you I had all of my joy in life, and now I am losing you both. There is nothing left to me." He felt as if his heart would break.

Sir Gawaine, lying there in the boat, realized that death had come for him at last. His knowledge that he faced the end brought him to his senses. He saw how he had wasted all these lives as well as his own for nothing but revenge.

"Yes, I have to die," he told his uncle, the King, "and it is my own fault. I was wilful and hasty, and sought only to harm the good knight, Launcelot. If he had not been banished, none of this unhappy war would have begun. I am the cause of all of our trouble, and I want to tell Launcelot so before I die."

They brought him paper and ink, and he wrote with great pain and weakness to Launcelot asking his forgiveness and begging him to return to England in all haste to help the good King put Mordred to flight.

Then he prayed Arthur to send for Launcelot, and to cherish him above all other knights. And when he had done all that he could to repair the damage he had made, he quietly died. His angry spirit was at peace at last.

But the trouble which he had stirred up went on as troubles do after the instigator is gone. Mordred pitched new fields of battle, and King Arthur fought him back. As the King's army gained power the people began to give back their allegiance to him. But he might well by now feel that their loyalty was easily shaken.

A great final battle was agreed upon. But the night before the battle the King had a clear and wonderful dream. It seemed to him that Sir

Sir Mordred

Gawaine came to him and said that God had per-
mitted him to give the King warning. If he entered upon this battle with Mordred, he would lose
his life.

"Within a month," he told Arthur, "Launcelot
will come over here to England with his knights
and rescue you. He will slay Mordred and his followers. Delay the battle for a month if you would
live." Then he disappeared.

The King called his knights and bishops and ad-
visors all together and told them of his dream.
Then he commanded two of his knights to make a
treaty with Mordred for one month offering him
anything he demanded in return.

It was no easy matter to win a treaty for
Mordred had by now collected a hundred thousand men. But at last he agreed if they would give
him Cornwall and Kent while the King was alive,
and after his death the whole of England. Mordred
did not sell his favors lightly.

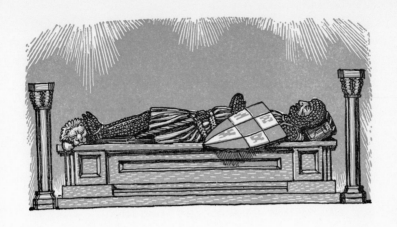

12

The Death of King Arthur

THE KNIGHTS NOW ARRANGED FOR A COURT OF arbitration, which was good sense. Each side should have fourteen members so that they could discuss peace in fair terms.

King Arthur agreed to the arrangement and

went into the field to meet Mordred. But neither
he nor Mordred trusted each other in the least.

"If you see any sword drawn," Arthur warned
his knights, "drive fiercely at Mordred and kill
him for I have no faith in him whatever."

Sir Mordred called his knights together. "If you
see any sword drawn," he told them, "rush instantly into battle and kill every knight who stands
before you. I do not trust this treaty."

The treaty, indeed, stood small chance of success with this attitude toward it from both sides.

The fourteen men from each side gathered on
the moor, and at a distance from them the troops
waited. The discussion started, wary, careful.
Around them the moor was quiet, at peace. Within
them distrust, hatred. But wine was brought and
they drank, though furtively, watching each
other.

Suddenly from behind a little heath bush an
adder darted and stung a knight on his foot. In-
stinctively, and with no thought of other harm, the
knight drew his sword to kill the adder.

It was enough. Instantly with the gleam of the

sword both sides were at each other. And such a battle as followed had never been seen in any land. Not an adder but fear had started this slaughter!

The men fought the whole day until at night a hundred thousand good knights lay dead in the moonlight. The moor was quiet again, and the small adder slipped back into its hole.

With the two knights left to him, Lucan and Bedivere, the King stood and stared at the carnage around him. He was filled with fury as he looked. It gave him no comfort that Sir Mordred stood, a shadowy figure against the darkening sky, alone with not one knight left to him.

When he saw Mordred leaning on his sword among a great heap of dead men, he cried aloud in his agony. "It may be that I have come to my end, but before I go I will kill this traitor who has brought about all of this woe. Give me my spear!"

Sir Lucan tried to dissuade him. "The man is alone," he said. "You have left him nothing but unhappiness. Remember your dream and what the spirit of Sir Gawaine warned you. Stop now at the end of this wicked day while you are still alive. There are three of us to live on, and with Mordred there is none."

But Arthur at the end of this long and terrible day was beyond any reason. He caught up his spear and started across the moor toward the lonely figure bent over its sword.

"Whether I live or die," he cried, "I shall never have a better chance than now. He shall not escape my hands." And he ran toward Mordred his voice loud in the quiet of the moor. "Traitor, your day of death has come!"

Mordred came out of his mourning and despair when he heard the voice. With his sword drawn in his hand he rushed at King Arthur. And so they fought, the deadliest fight of all. For neither had anything to live for now.

Neither had much strength either at the end of this long and terrible day. The battle was mercifully short. Arthur soon ran his spear through the body of Mordred who, when he felt his death's wound, gathered all of his strength and thrust his sword through the King's helmet. The two men fell on the blood-soaked ground, Mordred dead, Arthur unconscious.

Then Lucan and Bedivere, both of them weak from wounds, tried to lift Arthur and carry him away. Over and over again they heaved him up, and finally they got him to a little chapel near the edge of the sea. He rested there quietly until he heard rough voices of men on the moor.

"Go back, Lucan," he commanded, "and see what this noise means."

Poor Lucan, badly wounded, struggled back again. The moon was high now, and there in its light he saw a sorry sight. For robbers had come from all around to strip the dead of jewels and swords. And if the knight was not dead, they killed and stripped him.

Sick at the sight, Lucan hurried back to Arthur and begged him to let them bring him as quickly as possible to some safe town.

Arthur consented, but then he found that he was too weak to stand. Lucan and Bedivere lifted him, one on each side, and this was the last service which Lucan could ever do for his beloved

King. He fell dead in his effort. And King Arthur felt that his heart would break.

When Bedivere wept, Arthur said, "This is no time for mourning and weeping. If I could live I should mourn Sir Lucan forever. But my time is almost gone, and there is a task which you must do for me."

He unfastened his noble sword which had been at his side so long and held it out to Bedivere. "Take Excalibur, my good sword," said Arthur, "and go with it to the edge of the water. I charge you to throw my sword into that water, and then come again and tell me what you have seen."

"My lord," said Bedivere, "your command shall be done."

But as he walked toward the water his eyes saw all the beauty and riches of the sword, and he said to himself that no good could come of throwing away such jewels. So he hid the sword in a bush under a tree.

When he related how he had thrown the sword in the water, King Arthur asked what he saw.

"Oh, nothing," said Bedivere. "Nothing but waves and the wind."

"You have lied to me," said Arthur, and his weakness made the deceit hard to bear. "Go again quickly, and do as I have asked you."

Startled and a little ashamed, Bedivere hurried back to the tree where he had hidden the sword. He drew it out, caught the gleam of its jewels, and said, "It is a sin and a shame to throw away that noble sword."

He thrust it back into the bushes and returned to King Arthur who lay waiting, cold and filled with anguish. Again Bedivere told him that he had thrown the sword into the water, and again Arthur asked him what he saw.

"Nothing at all," said Bedivere, "except the water and the waves lapping the shore."

But now, his weakness overcome by his anger and despair, Arthur drove at Bedivere. "You are a traitor," he cried, "and you have betrayed me twice. I could never have believed that you would deceive me for the riches of a sword. You who have been my dear and close friend! Now go quickly, for I have taken cold lying here while I waited for you."

He sat up and pointed toward the water, stern in

his wrath. "Go now," he said. "And if you do not as I bid I will slay you with my own hands. For the sake of my rich sword, you would like to see me dead." He sank back on the ground, empty of all hope of friendship.

Then Bedivere ran swiftly to the hidden sword, seized it, and threw it as far into the water as he could reach. Its beauty had no more charm for him, and he was filled with shame.

As the sword curved down to meet the surface of the lake, an arm and a hand reached high out of the water, caught the sword, shook it three times, and vanished carrying it into the deep.

Sir Bedivere returned to his King and told him what he had seen. He saw with fear and dread the weakness of Arthur. Because of his disloyalty his King was spent with long waiting.

"Help me now," said Arthur, "for I have stayed too long."

Sir Bedivere lifted the King on his back and carried him to the water's edge. There was little enough that he could do now for his King.

When they reached the bank they saw there a

King Arthur was laid on a barge near the water's edge.

small barge. In it were three queens and their ladies in black hoods, and they all sorrowed together when they saw King Arthur.

But to Arthur the barge was a place of refuge. "Lift me aboard," he told Bedivere, and the knight put him gently down. Then Arthur laid his head in the lap of his sister, the queen, and rested as if he had come home. They rowed away from the land.

Bedivere called out, standing alone on the beach, "What will become of me, alone here in the land of my enemies? What will now happen to me?"

"Do as well as you can," Arthur answered. "For you have left in me no trust on which I could lean. I will now go to the vale of Avilion, and if you hear no more of me, pray for my soul."

Sir Bedivere stood on the lonely shore and watched the barge move slowly out of sight until there was only blue water and blue sky left for him to see. Then shaken with sorrow and fear he turned toward the woods and tried to find refuge.

All night long he pushed his way through the black trees with nothing to accompany him but the thoughts of his treachery and of the harm he had done his King. When daylight came his heart lifted. Ahead of him he could see in the dim light a small chapel and a hermitage.

He walked softly into the chapel, and there he saw a hermit praying beside a new-made grave. The hermit lifted his head, and Bedivere saw that it was the Bishop of Canterbury whom Sir Mordred had banished when he had tried to end the warfare.

"Who lies there in that grave?" asked Bedivere, and dreaded the answer.

"I am not sure," answered the Bishop. "At midnight last night a number of ladies all in black brought to me for sacrament a dead body. They left with me a hundred tapers to burn. He must have been a great man."

It was enough. Sir Bedivere knew well that his good King lay there buried in this chapel. He wished that he might never go away from him, and begged the Bishop to allow him to stay there where he could fast and pray.

"You are welcome to stay with me," the hermit replied, "for I know you better than you think.

You are Sir Bedivere, brother of Lucan, who have both served our King."

Then Bedivere put on poor clothes and stayed with the Bishop in his hermitage, serving him well and perhaps finding comfort in his prayers. For it was hard to forget that Arthur had died not trusting him.

So strong was Arthur in the hearts of his people, and so sure were they that they could always depend upon him in time of need, that many of them would not accept his death. They believed that he would come again and win the holy cross. They could not let him go.

Yet others tell of his tomb and the words written upon it: Hic jacet Arthurus Rex quondam Rex que futurus. "Here lies Arthur, King that was and King that shall be."

Perhaps they were all right, for though a great man had come and gone, he is still a king in the hearts of the people and the deeds which he did still influence their own deeds. And so he has come again and again through the ages, King that shall be.

13

His Truth Goes Marching On

THE NEWS CAME SLOWLY TO LAUNCELOT ACROSS the sea, bitter news which he could hardly bear. He heard with anger which shook his very heart that Sir Mordred had been crowned king of England, and that he would not let Arthur land in his own country. He heard with such anxiety that he was nearly mad about Mordred's siege to the Tower of London because the Queen refused to wed him.

He could not know with news so slow to travel that Guinevere had found a refuge for herself. When she heard that King Arthur was dead after the terrible battle, she lost all of her sharp zest in living. She stole quietly away with five of her ladies to the safety and peace of the convent at Almesbury, as far as she could get from London. There she became a nun, and lived with fasting and prayers and good deeds until she was made abbess. From one life she had stepped into another so different that her friends scarcely knew her. Of her past life which had been the source of so much torture to those who loved her, she tried not to think.

But Launcelot was already on his way to her. He had as usual overcome his anger with action. He had gathered together his knights on ships and galleys and set sail for England in all haste. The ships were far too slow for him, and he paced their decks with his impatience.

As soon as he landed at Dover he called to the people on the shore, "Where is King Arthur? Is it well with him?"

Many voices in confusion battered the harsh news on his ears. His King was dead, a hundred thousand had died that day, the good Sir Gawaine was slain, and, the only hope out of all the carnage, the King had killed Sir Mordred.

Launcelot listened, and felt as if the very foundations of his life had been shaken from under him. "These tidings," he said, "are the worst that ever came to me," and he hardly knew which way to turn.

But there were certain things which he must do, and again Launcelot turned his sorrows into action. He made the people show him the tomb of Sir Gawaine at the castle of Dover, and there he prayed for his old friend's soul, and offered a rich mass.

Then he called his knights together and spoke to them. "I thank you all for coming to this country with me," he said. "We are too late, but against death we cannot rebel. Now I shall ride

alone to find my lady Guinevere for I hear that
she is ill and in pain. If I do not return in fifteen days, go aboard your ships and sail back to
your country."

The knights tried to dissuade him, but he would
not listen. "I shall go by myself," he repeated.
"And no man nor child shall go with me."

And go he did, alone, traveling west and search-
ing for some clue about Queen Guinevere. For a
week he rode until at last he came to a nunnery.
He walked into the cloister, and there he saw
Guinevere.

When she looked up and saw Launcelot standing there, she could not believe her senses which
seemed all to leave her. Faint and weak, she called
her ladies to her. They supported her on either
side and listened to her command, "Bring this
knight to me."

Launcelot came, his heart trembling at the sight
of her face so white, so stern. And yet so dear.

"Through this man and me," she said to the
ladies, "war has come and the noblest knights in
the world have been killed. Because of our love a
good and wise king has been slain. And so, Sir

Launcelot, I must never see you again. Go to your country, take a wife, and live in happiness. And I shall pray here for my sins."

"No." Launcelot spoke. "That I shall never do." For now he knew what was ahead of him. "Like you I shall forsake the world and enter a hermitage of peace if one will receive me."

So they parted, the two who had loved each other so well, and with the parting their hearts broke. They had lived for love of each other and now they were willing to die. They could not know that comfort would come to each of them from the good deeds and quiet living of the next six years.

But now Sir Launcelot took his horse and rode all day and all night through the dark forest. He wept in his sorrow and despair. Then through the silence of the dawn he heard a little bell ring as if for mass. He rode toward the sound and found between two cliffs a hermitage and a chapel. He tied his horse to the gate and heard mass.

Then he saw that the priest who sang mass was the Bishop of Canterbury, and that with him was his old friend, Sir Bedivere. His heart lifted, and he fell upon his knees begging the Bishop to let him stay there in peace.

The Bishop said, "I will gladly." For he was a wise old man, and he knew what Launcelot needed. He gave him the habit of the monk, and taught him the life of prayer and good deeds. It was a new life for Launcelot, but in it he found more happiness than he could have dreamed.

Curiously enough, some of the other knights who were not satisfied to sail away without knowing the whereabouts of their leader, Sir Launcelot, rode through the woods as he had done. They heard the clear small bell ring for mass, and listened as he had done. And like him, they begged to stay so that Launcelot had with him seven of his friends who, like him, found richness of living in service to others. Their bodies grew thin from fasting but their spirits were strong.

Six years went quietly past, and at the end of them Launcelot had a vision. It came to him three times in the night, and he knew that it was true. It charged him to go at once to Almesbury where he would find Queen Guinevere dead. It commanded him to come for her and bury her beside her husband, the good King Arthur.

Sir Launcelot obeyed. With the seven monks, his friends, he started for Almesbury, thirty miles away. The knights were so weak from fasting that it took them two days on foot. And when they reached the convent they found that she had died only a half hour before. Her ladies said that she had told them that Sir Launcelot would come for her to bury her beside her King.

But for Launcelot, the priest, there were no more tears. He looked at Guinevere's peaceful face and sighed. Then as priest he went about his final duties for his lady. With solemn masses and deep devotion he took her to Glastonbury and laid her where she wanted to be, beside her husband who had been England's noblest king.

Launcelot went back to his hermitage but his weakened body could endure no more. Yet his departure was not sad. One night the Bishop woke them all with his laughter. They hurried to him, and he told them that in his merry dream he had seen Launcelot heaved into heaven by more angels than ever he had seen men. And the gates of heaven opened for him.

They hastened to Launcelot's bedside and found him dead. But they did not mourn for they knew that he was glad to go. They carried him as he had wished to his castle where he had had so much happiness, Joyous Gard. With simple devotions they left him there in the small chapel, at peace at last. Then the knights went back with the Bishop to his hermitage. They missed their friend, but they were glad that he was free. His good works went on through them.

Now the time had come when England must have a new king. Out of the wisdom which they had learned through the long reign of King Arthur and his knights, the people chose well. No longer could a Sir Mordred lead them with false promises. King Arthur had shown them the way to a freedom which they had never had.

In Cornwall there was a noble knight, Sir Constantine, who was young and strong and had shown great promise. They named him king, and he fulfilled all their hopes. He was a good man, and a great.

He had heard about the Bishop of Canterbury and his exile to the hermitage in the woods. He sent

So they parted, the two who had loved each other so well.

for him and restored him to his bishopric. He asked the other knights of the hermitage to come, too, but they had been away from the problems of the world too long. They did not wish to go.

Sir Bedivere stayed on as a hermit in the forest chapel as long as he lived. The other knights lived in their own countries, and when the Turks assailed them they fought them well. There were times when the life of the hermit had to be exchanged for fighting.

King Arthur and his Knights of the Round Table left the world as time passed on. Yet they left it a different place, and so they have never quite gone away from us. We listen to tales of their valor and strength in days when such qualities were rare, and our hearts are lifted with hope that the same great forces will serve us in our need of today.

Youth seizes the banner of justice and right, and holds it aloft. With the whole world behind him, alert to follow, he is ready like King Arthur to carry on the struggle toward progress, to advance toward civilization for all the people. All strength of mind and spirit go with him!

Have you read the World Landmarks?

★

LANDMARK BOOKS